THE LIFE OF
ELLEN H. RICHARDS

Ellen H Richards

THE LIFE OF
ELLEN H. RICHARDS

1842-1911

BY

CAROLINE L. HUNT

Anniversary Edition

American Home Economics Association
Washington, D. C.
1958

FOREWORD TO THE ANNIVERSARY EDITION

THE very fact that a biography of Ellen H. Richards is still warmly welcomed speaks for the affirmed greatness of the founder of home economics. In the decades since her death, the projects that were warm with her personality when this biography was first written have gained stature and life of their own. Higher education for women has been achieved, but questioning minds in the tradition of Mrs. Richards still seek to direct its clearest rays to the life of our times. Homemaking has become increasingly scientific, yet the intellectual challenge so stimulated by Mrs. Richards grows stronger each year. The focus of the academic and scientific approach on the field of homemaking, which climaxed Mrs. Richards' work, has created a new profession, honored at home and around the world.

That this new edition of the biography of Mrs. Richards coincides so nearly with the fiftieth anniversary of the American Home Economics Association is further tribute to the founder of the profession and first president of the Association. It can only emphasize what was already apparent in the first few years after Mrs. Richards' death—that, great as were her contributions to the idea of higher education for women, her unique contribution was her vision of higher education linked to the traditional area of women's activity—homemaking.

Home economics—as its founders saw it—and as it exists today—is concerned on the one hand with man's immediate physical environment and on the other with his nature as a social being, and is the study especially of the relation between these two factors.

The physical environment to be conquered in Mrs. Richards' day included some of the most elementary aspects of household sanitation. Today, the environment may be characterized by highly complicated machines to be mastered, but the ultimate goal is the same—an environment that supports and contributes to the well-being of people, as individuals and as members of a family and society.

The nature of man as a social being and his relationship to his physical environment are increasingly the emphases in home economics today. The service of science to the most intimate well-being of individuals is not lessened by the potentialities of science directed to man's challenge to the universe. That individuals must first be strong within themselves and within the family and social unit is as true today as it was more than half a century ago when the possibilities of a profession devoted to this goal were first visualized.

In the decades since the formation of the American Home Economics Association, home economics has become both a recognized field of study and a profession. Drawing from the various basic sciences and the arts, it has synthesized a body of subject matter and developed an educational movement with related research, services, and occupational areas.

As an academic subject, home economics is now presented for bachelor's degrees in nearly 500 colleges and universities; master's degrees are offered in more than 100 institutions; and doctoral degrees in 15. The pressure for more and more persons with the higher degrees is one of the strongest demands on the profession at the Association's fifty-year mark. Without highly trained research workers, subject matter cannot be developed and extended. Without well-trained administrators and faculty, higher education cannot continue its development nor maintain its position as a springboard from which the creative minds of this era may set forth as did the first leaders in Mrs. Richards' day.

Home economics today includes in its subject matter several areas of study and research which the Association usually classifies as: art applied to the home, family relations and child development, family economics and home management, food and nutrition, housing and household equipment, and textiles and clothing. Each of these areas has achieved breadth and richness even beyond the expectations of the founders of the profession; none has yet come within sight of the boundaries to which it can be extended by intelligence, imagination, and research. Each is still developing its function of improving the relationship between man as a social being and his environment. Each renews and refreshes itself automatically from the life of our times. Each finds an eager audience and many channels to that audience.

Home economics occupations—limited almost completely to teaching in the early years of the profession—now are as varied as homemaking itself and as the talents of the seven or eight thousand young persons who earn home economics degrees each year. Though full-time homemaking is without doubt the occupation of the largest number of these graduates, in 1955 the American Home Economics Association estimated that there were approximately 64,000 professionally employed home economists in the United States. Teaching accounted for more than 41,000, with 26,000 of these in public secondary schools, 500 in other secondary schools, 250 in nursery schools and kindergartens, 11,000 in adult education programs in public school systems, and 3400 in college teaching, administration, and research connected with colleges. The Federal Extension Service of the U. S. Department of Agriculture employed 5,000; hospital dietetics, 8,000; other food service and institution administration, 4,000; business, 3400; social welfare and public health, 700; and research work in the U. S. Department of Agriculture, 140.

In addition to these professional positions in the United States itself, home economists from the United States are employed in all parts of the world—in educational and technical assistance programs under the auspices of the United Nations, national governments, foundations, or religious groups. Such assignments—like the numbers of persons from abroad who are studying home economics in the United States—have greatly increased in number since World War II. One result has been that an increasing number of the people of the world are learning to improve their well-being through the principles of home economics applied to their own circumstances. Another important result is the enrichment of home economics in the United States through this cultural exchange.

The ability to contribute to the social and cultural environment of the family as well as to its physical surroundings has, over the years, become one of the most treasured characteristics of home economics. One of the prime objectives of the profession and of the American Home Economics Association is to continue and to expand this capacity throughout the future.

* * * * *

In the preparation of this anniversary edition of *The Life of Ellen H. Richards,* some of the excerpts from letters, originally included in the text, have been transferred to Appendixes in order to throw more emphasis on the progression of Mrs. Richards' work toward the founding of home economics. The two chapters "At College" in the previous printings have been combined into one chapter. A few comments on certain conditions existing at the time of the writing of the biography and which are now outdated, have been deleted. At several places in the text, tenses have been changed and such terms as "now" or "is still . . ." have been modified for ease of reading. However, the reader should keep in mind that the biography was written in 1911 and that the perspective on Mrs. Richards' work is of that date.

MARY HAWKINS
Editor of Publications
American Home Economics Association

Washington, D. C.
January 1958

FOREWORD TO THE SIXTH PRINTING
[June 1942]

IN THE thirty years since this book was first published it has made a lasting place for itself in the literature of educational developments, especially the increasingly important phases that deal with home and family life and what are now sometimes called consumer problems. Like the reports of the Lake Placid Conference, out of which the American Home Economics Association developed in 1908, and like Isabel Bevier's *Home Economics in Education,* Caroline Hunt's *Life of Ellen H. Richards* ranks as indispensable source material on the beginnings of home economics. For several years the book has been out of print, despite a steady if limited demand. To make it again available, the American Home Economics Association has purchased the plates from M. Barrows and Company. It is a pleasant coincidence that this new edition appears in 1942, the centenary of Mrs. Richards' birth.

The relation of Mrs. Richards to the original publishers, Whitcomb and Barrows, deserves a word of mention. The Barrows of the firm was Mary Barrows, sister of Anna Barrows. She and Mr. Whitcomb were in close touch with the leaders of the early home economics movement—in fact a note to the 1918 printing of the *Life of Ellen H. Richards* says of her, "Our existence as a firm is due to her belief in the need for specialized service in the literature of Home Economics. Our first publications were her books. Through seven years of development our best business asset was her good will." Later the firm name was changed to M. Barrows and Company, which it still retains though Mary Barrows has retired and the character of its publications has somewhat altered.

Five printings of the book have been made, the latest in 1931. The first (1912) edition included more illustrations than the others. The one issued in 1918 was called "Conservation Edition," but it did not differ from the others except by the insertion of a brief foreword calling attention to the fact that as early as 1885 Mrs. Richards was pioneering to promote the same principles of conservation as were being used as the basis of conservation campaigns in wartime. Since the book was written various things have happened that seem worth chronicling here because they show the continuing influence of Mrs. Richards' constructive, inspiring thought. Very appropriately, several of them have to do with research along lines in which she was a pioneer or at least a prophet.

In 1911 the Association to Aid Scientific Research by Women, which maintained the so-called American Women's Table at Naples, named the prize of $1000, which it was awarding annually, the Ellen Richards Research Prize. This was in recognition of Mrs. Richards' work as chairman of the committee on awards since the Association was established in 1900. Six regular awards were made, three to women in the United States and three in England. In 1921 a special award of $2000 was made to Madame Curie. Grants were again made in 1928 and in 1931-32, after which the Association abolished the fund.

In 1913 a fund of $15,000 was presented to the Massachusetts Institute of Technology, to be known as the Ellen H. Richards Research Fund, and to be used for research in sanitary chemistry, the subject which she had taught so effectively at the Institute. The grants, which are still being made annually and are known as Ellen H. Richards Memorial Fellowships, carry $500 from the fund, supplemented by a further grant from the Institute to cover full tuition. Thanks to this generous co-operation, part of the interest on the fund has been returned to it, so that it now amounts to about $23,000. For the first two years the work was under the direction of Dr. John H. Norton, son of Mrs. Alice Peloubet Norton, a close friend of Mrs. Richards and editor of the *Journal of Home Economics* from 1915 to 1921.

The beginnings of the Ellen H. Richards Memorial Fund collected by the American Home Economics Association are mentioned by Miss Hunt in her last chapter. The money was raised during the years following Mrs. Richards' death and included contributions not only from her friends and associates but from hundreds of younger home economists. In the early days some of the income was used for publications to promote the fund, but since 1925 it has all gone into fellowships for graduate study in some field of home economics. These are administered by a committee of the Association, and to receive one is considered a high honor among home economics students.

The Ellen H. Richards Institute at Pennsylvania State College, established about 1940 for graduate research in problems of food, clothing, and shelter, operates on funds received partly from public sources and partly from industry and business but its name and the high quality of its work reflect the inspiration of Mrs. Richards' vision and example.

The division of euthenics at Vassar College, established in 1923, with research and graduate work added in 1924, is her alma mater's tribute to her philosophy and shows that the latter is not out of harmony with the liberal arts tradition. Similar work is given in several other liberal arts colleges, sometimes under one name, sometimes another. As Miss Hunt tells us, the word euthenics was coined by Mrs. Richards; it is gradually making its way into college catalogues and dictionaries.

On December 3, 1928, the eighty-sixth anniversary of her birth, a bronze tablet, presented by her friends, was unveiled in her memory at the Massachusetts Institute of Technology. It carries a bas-relief portrait by Bashka Paeff and a few words to suggest her academic and social achievements. A description of it and the tributes paid at the unveiling appeared in the *Journal of Home Economics* for June 1929.

It is not only learned institutions that keep green the memory of "the patron saint of home economics." Her birthday, December 3, is celebrated as Ellen H. Richards or Home Economics Day in many schools and colleges, and the thousands of home economics clubs throughout the country frequently devote a meeting to her life and work. For these the girls have worked out clever skits and other programs, a few of them available through the American

Home Economics Association. Pictures of her are in steady demand from future home economists.

Though many may not have heard her name, the public now recognizes the real social value of the movement which Mrs. Richards was so influential in starting. This is not the place to review the development of home economics in schools and colleges, in agricultural extension work, or in other types of adult education. In these days of national emergency, however, it may not be unfitting to recall how much the professional children of Mrs. Richards contributed to the civilian effort during the First World War, when they suddenly found themselves leaders in food and other conservation campaigns; or how, during the dark days after the collapse of 1929, they were called on to steer families through the homely, day-by-day difficulties of unemployment and became a recognized force in the rural rehabilitation program. As we look ahead in 1942, we can be confident that home economists will help solve many of the confusing problems that will confront all of us in days of shortages, of changing incomes, of disrupted families and ways of living. As before, they will follow Mrs. Richards' teaching that true economy in the home depends on the intelligent selection and use of goods and services, on the careful weighing of competing needs, and on a scientifically valid foundation of fact for decisions on these everyday questions. And they will be heartened to remember how she put her theories into practice, not only in her professional work, but in her own pleasant, smooth-running, hospitable home.

Although in writing the life of Mrs. Richards, Miss Hunt naturally kept herself in the background, this foreword owes it to her readers to include a few lines about her and her other work. Born in 1861 in Chicago, she was educated in public schools there and in Evanston and attended Northwestern University, interrupting her college course by two years of teaching. After taking her degree, she taught physics and chemistry, then did graduate work at Northwestern and at the University of Chicago. From 1894 to 1896 she lived in the congenial and stimulating atmosphere of Hull House while she was making dietary studies among her foreign neighbors for the United States Department of

Agriculture. Then followed five years as head of the home economics work at Lewis Institute and another five in a similar position at the University of Wisconsin. For a while she was on the staff of *LaFollette's Magazine* and developed great skill in stating scientific facts in attractive popular terms. In 1909 she joined the staff of what was then known as the Nutrition Investigations and later a part of the Office (now the Bureau) of Home Economics in the United States Department of Agriculture. She remained there, with brief intermissions, until her death in January 1927.

Popular methods of presenting food facts have developed so much during the last fifteen or twenty years that it is hard to realize how original and imaginative were her ways of "translating calories, protein, carbohydrates, and vitamins into terms of well-balanced, appetizing meals," or what our present methods would be if she had not blazed so good a trail.

During her years in Chicago, Madison, and later in Washington, she worked actively with the people of the Lake Placid Conference and the American Home Economics Association and presented stimulating papers in which she developed her fine philosophy of homemaking. Nowhere did she state this better than in her delightful *Revaluations,* originally read at Lake Placid and later printed by Whitcomb and Barrows. After her death it was republished in a limited memorial edition by some of her friends and distributed by the American Home Economics Association, together with a short biographical sketch. The latter is perhaps the best there is available, but it is far too brief to show her warm human interests, her wide culture, her independence of thought, her scorn of empty conventions, her unsparing generosity. Because of her literary skill, her sympathetic imagination, and her close relations with Mrs. Richards and her work, Caroline Hunt was a happy choice as biographer of her friend and leader.

HELEN WOODARD ATWATER

Editor, *Journal of Home Economics,* 1923-1941

Washington, D. C.
June 1942

CONTENTS

INTRODUCTION

O N THE evening of the second of April, nineteen hundred and eleven, a group of friends and co-workers of Mrs. Richards, several of whom had come from far distant places to attend her funeral, met at the College Club in Boston.

Gathered together under the shadow of their great sorrow, they told each other what Mrs. Richards had done for them. Each had a characteristic saying of hers to repeat, or an anecdote illustrating her unfailing helpfulness to relate, but chiefly they spoke of how her call to them had always been in the direction of the large outgiving life.

Strangely enough the outlook even at that time, so soon after her death, was not backward, but forward. They asked even then what they could do to carry on the work that she had laid down. As the evening wore on, the suggestion was made that one way of doing this would be by giving permanent form to what had been said there so informally, and the hope was expressed that they and others who had known the insipiration of her personal influence might have an opportunity to show her to the world as they had seen her.

Professor Richards, hearing of this conference, asked to have a committee of persons representing Mrs. Richards' various interests formed for the purpose of advising with him about the preparation of a memorial volume. The committee was formed with Isabel F. Hyams as chairman, to whom, because of "a daily companionship of twenty years which had sustained hands that were often weary," Mrs. Richards had dedicated her last book. Other members were Mrs. Mary Hinman Abel, editor of the *Journal of Home Economics;* Isabel Bevier, who succeeded Mrs. Richards as president of the American Home Economics Association; Anna Barrows, of Teachers College; Florence Cushing, who represented the Associate Alumnæ of Vassar College and the Association of Collegiate Alumnæ, and who had been a student in the Woman's Laboratory; James P. Munroe, of the Corporation of the Massachusetts Institute of Technology; Frances Stern, who had been Mrs. Richards' secretary; Lillian Jameson, also secretary to Mrs. Richards; Jean Swain, to whom the stenographic work was to be intrusted, and myself.

The result of the conference of this committee with Professor Richards, and of his earnest desire to smooth out all financial difficulties of the undertaking in order that he might share with others the life-giving influence which had been his for nearly forty years, was a determination to prepare this volume.

In response to a request for material which might be of service, many letters written by Mrs. Richards were received, and also many records and personal testimonies. For all of these we who have been more closely concerned in the preparation of the book wish to acknowledge our indebtedness. We hesitate, however, to express our thanks, because we feel that all, near and far, have been working together for one end, and that what others have done has been not for us but for her. We hesitate, too, to name any of these who have assisted us because of the hopelessness of naming all. A few, however, must be mentioned here.

We are indebted to Anna A. Swallow and to other relatives of Mrs. Richards for the record of her early life; to Mrs. Laura E. Richards and Rosalind Richards for facts about her personal and home life; to her classmates, Mrs. Flora Hughes and Anna Mineah, and other college friends for a large number of valuable letters; to the Woman's Education Association of Boston for permission to examine its early records; to Margaret E. Dodd for bringing to light many facts about the Studies at Home; to Dean Marion Talbot for the story of her connection with the Association of Collegiate Alumnæ; to Dr. C. F. Langworthy for information about her connection with the work of the Department of Agriculture; to many graduates of the Massachusetts Institute of Technology and many of the faculty for facts concerning her connection with that institution; to Margaret Maltby for many letters written by Mrs. Richards during her later years; to Louisa P. Hewins, of Jamaica Plain, a friend whom circumstances made the companion of her leisure rather than of her labors, for the story of many of her lighter moments. These are but a few of those who have helped; how far we have fallen short of acknowledging our full indebtedness the text will indicate by showing the breadth of her activities and how far our researches have necessarily extended.

Editors, revisers, stenographer, publishers, illustrator, printer, all of whom came under her influence, have worked together to prepare this book as a memorial to her. If it is lacking in unity because of this wide co-operation, it must surely approach more nearly to completeness.

CAROLINE L. HUNT

THE LIFE OF
ELLEN H. RICHARDS

Chapter I

CHILDHOOD

THE unseen and the untried have ever lured adventurous and courageous spirits, calling forth in every age explorers, who have this in common that they set forth with glad feet and expectant faces toward that which lies beyond the knowledge or experience of their times. But that which they seek, whether it shall be an undiscovered country, a new field of knowledge, or an untried way of living, is determined by inner impulses and outward circumstances. These unite to create multiple forms of the exploring type.

The girl-child of adventurous spirit born to rural New England during the middle of the nineteenth century naturally chose as her field of exploration new modes of helpfulness and of service. This choice was almost inevitable at that time in that region, for earnestness, conscientiousness, and unyielding devotion to duty were breathed in with the air of puritan New England, and self-sacrifice was demanded of women both by tradition and by public opinion. But many of the older forms of labor which had been women's contribution to family and community life were being rendered unnecessary, while at the same time enlarging means of communication and widening educational opportunities were opening to them a whole new world, and were suggesting to those who happened to be of adventurous spirit the presence of fresh fields of usefulness lying beyond the vision and waiting to be explored. Inner impulses toward pioneering, as well as those toward helpfulness, were likely in rural New England seventy years ago to be quickened by the outward conditions of life.

Into these changing social conditions Ellen Swallow was born on a New England farm at a time not far from the middle of the nineteenth century. As she grew, her two most marked physical characteristics, a steadfast look from large, thoughtful gray eyes, and a quickness of motion and of speech, came to be the outward evidences of the two great passions of her life—a longing for usefulness and a love of pioneering. These passions her early life in an isolated community and among profoundly religious people doubtless tended to strengthen and intensify. She was destined to give herself for others, but to do it in unique ways, and after the fashion of explorers, joyously and enthusiastically, so that the record of her life and labors is the story of happy excursions into fresh fields of service.

The Swallow homestead, where she was born, was situated near the village of Dunstable, which is part of a town of the same name in Northern Massachusetts, on the New Hampshire line. From the place where the old home once stood one may look out over the fields to a small burying ground where Ensign John Swallow, who died in the year 1776, lies buried. "Ensign John," as his descendants fondly call him, was the first of the Swallow name to find his way to the little settlement of Dunstable, in whose records his name frequently appears. He was the grandson of Ambrose Swallow, who was born in England, but who was living in Massachusetts as early as 1666. There is a tradition that the Swallow family had earlier married into a French family named Larnard. If this be true, and it is confirmed by the fact that several of the headstones in the old family cemetery bear the name Larnard, a small amount of French blood must have run in Ellen Swallow's veins.

There is a sense in which it must be said that Dunstable found its way to Ensign John instead of Ensign John's finding his way to Dunstable, for in 1753 the petition of himself and seven of his neighbors, then resident in the adjacent town of Groton, to be annexed "with their Families & Estates" to Dunstable, was granted, and the boundaries of the town were extended so as to include them. The purpose of this step on the part of the petitioners was not to improve their worldly prospects, but "to Joine with Dunstable in settling the gospell and all other affairs hart & hand in case Dunstable would meet them in erecting a meting house in center of Lands or center of Travel."

The town of Dunstable, which had been incorporated in

the year 1673, was surveyed in 1674. The boundaries by which it was marked off were determined, after the homely fashion of the times, by the natural features of the landscape, and being described as passing from pine tree to hilltop or from meadow to stream or pond, they give an index to the varied though quiet beauty of the place, and to its charm, which to this day is peculiarly unspoiled. At the first town meeting of which there is any record it was voted to call a minister, and to proceed with the building of the meeting house. In that generation affairs of the spirit were considered to be the concern of the whole community.

But troublous times were in store for the little band of settlers in Dunstable, for the town, having been cut from a wilderness and lying at the farthest point which the tide of immigration following the Merrimac River had reached, was in an exposed position, and the inhabitants were continually attacked, not only by Indians, but also by wild beasts. We read that in 1688 Samuel Gould was appointed dog whipper for the meeting house, an office which was indispensable because the settlers were obliged to take their dogs to church with them for protection. So fierce were the attacks of the Indians that the population was at one time reduced to a single person, the remainder having been killed or having fled to places of safety. But the pioneers were not to be vanquished. Those who had fled speedily returned, and having fortified their houses brought back their families. From that time on the population steadily increased; not very rapidly, however, for by the year 1753, when Ensign John cast his lot with the town, its inhabitants numbered only two hundred and fifty. But though few in number they were great in spirit, for in winning the wilderness and converting it into fertile farms, in removing the boulders with which the fields were strewn, and which an early history of the town says "were doubtless placed there by a Titantic force for a beneficent purpose," and in warding off attacks of their enemies, they had grown a sturdy and courageous people.

Ensign John's desire to see the gospel well settled in Dunstable was evidently taken seriously, for he was almost immediately appointed a member of a committee to complete the meeting house by supplying it with "26 windows,

23 of sd windows to Be 24 squares of glass in Each window, the 2 gavel End windows to Be 15 squairs Each & the pulpit window to be Left to the Descretion of the parish committe." It was he, too, who in 1757 built the house which was the birthplace of successive generations of the Swallow family. This house stood until 1882, when it was burned to the ground and replaced by another on nearly the same site. Ensign John's son, Peter, was one of a little band of men which Dunstable gave out of her poverty to serve in the War of Independence. He had a son Archelaus, and Archelaus' son, Peter, was the father of Ellen.

Peter Swallow, the second, was born on June 27, 1813, the oldest child of Archelaus and Susanna Kendall Swallow. Having scholarly tastes, he early began to look about him for an education, and by good fortune he was led to the academy at New Ipswich, New Hampshire. The good fortune was his and also the world's, for it was in New Ipswich that he found his future wife, Fanny Gould Taylor, and there the two families from which Ellen Swallow was to draw her strength and power were united. Mr. Swallow and Miss Taylor were married on May 9, 1839, and on December 3, 1842, their only child, Ellen Henrietta, was born.

Before as well as after graduating from the academy, Mr. Swallow taught in the neighboring towns of Pepperell, Tyngsborough, and Nashua, and one certificate of fitness to teach shows that when nineteen years old he traveled as far from home as Western Ohio. After his marriage he made his home in one end of his father's house, and in 1845 his father deeded to him half the farm and half the house. For ten or twelve years he followed the double occupation of teaching and farming, occupations which demanded his time during most of the year, but left leisure in the early spring. The month of March was often spent by him and his family in trips to New Hampshire, Vermont, or Maine for the purpose of visiting relatives. These journeys were made by team, and as they were taken at the time of year when the roads were likely to be worst, they were full of adventure. Fifty years afterwards his daughter wrote: "One of my earliest recollections is of my father's reply to my mother's anxiety lest we should get overturned in the sleigh on the snow-drifted country roads—'Where any one else has been, there I can go.' " "This," she continued, "is not a bad working motto, but adventurous spirits go beyond this and do what has never been done before," which expresses well the quality of adventuresomeness and love of exploration which in the daughter was added to the will and courage inherited from her father.

Mr. Swallow remained on the farm until 1859, when for the purpose of giving his daughter an academy education he moved to the neighboring town of Westford and opened a store. From that time until his sudden death in 1871, he was engaged in one form or another of trade; but whether because his interests were in books rather than in business, or for some other reason, he seems never to have been very successful.

The following extract from a letter written by Ellen Swallow to her mother while she was at Vassar gives a clew to one of her father's characteristics:

"I think father would be delighted to see Miss Mitchell lecturing me, as she did this morning, because I ignored the one one-hundredth of a second in an astronomical calculation. 'While you are doing it, you might as well do it to a nicety.' " It is said that no household task in the Swallow family was ever performed with such nicety as to meet with the father's unreserved approval. And yet this interest in details seems not to have been associated in him, as it often is, with narrowness of vision, for he was his daughter's most ardent supporter in her efforts to gain a college education and a scientific training at a time when such education and training were almost unknown among women.

Ellen Swallow's mother, Fanny Gould Taylor, was born in New Ipswich on April 9, 1817, the fourth daughter and sixth child of Samuel Taylor and Persis Jones. She was descended on her father's side from William Taylor, who came to this country from England about 1640, and after prospecting a little settled in Concord, Massachusetts, where several generations of his descendants tilled the soil. It was her grandfather, Thaddeus Taylor, who first came to New Ipswich. In the middle of the winter of 1776, with his wife, Bridget Walton, and four small children, he moved into an unfinished house on a hill in the southwestern part of the town. Here the family endured great hardship while the home was being finished and the "rough and rocky farm subdued." In this house "over the mountains," as it was described in a history of New Ipswich, Mrs. Swallow was born.

The Taylor family and many of the families into which it married showed a remarkable tendency toward longevity. Mrs. Swallow's father lived to be eighty-one and her mother to be eighty-eight. Thaddeus Taylor, the grandfather, was eighty-one when he died and his wife eighty-five. The ages of six of their nine children averaged over ninety years at the time of death, and one son, Oliver Swain Taylor, lived to be four months over one hundred years of age. Lydia Treadway, the grandmother of Mrs. Swallow's mother, lived to be ninety-four and to gather about her two hundred and thirty-three descendants. It may be that this tendency toward long life was in some way transmuted into that wonderful physical endurance which carried Ellen Swallow through a delicate childhood, and later made it seem as if she were living the lives of ten people and incidentally doing their work.

Deft and dainty were the adjectives most often applied to Mrs. Swallow. To her dexterity, which was shown in all traditionally feminine occupations, may doubtless be traced the carefulness of manipulation which helped to make her daughter successful in one of the most exacting of all forms of chemical work, water analysis. The mother's daintiness in dress impressed all who saw her, even in later years, when sickness and suffering would have made carelessness excusable.

From references to Ellen in letters received by her father and mother during her childhood, we may infer that she was one of those active yet dainty little creatures upon whose quick, quiet motions it is always a delight for grown people to look. "How is little Ellen?" one cousin wrote. "I often think of her; what a pretty, interesting, amusing little thing she is." And another: "I wish she were here; I should like no better plaything."

As she grew, she came perilously near being a tomboy, if, in fact, she did not quite step over the line. This was a sore trial to her mother, who wished to train the little feet to walk demurely, and the hands to love indoor and feminine occupations. But fortunately there came along a wise physician, who, noticing the frailty of the child, said that if she were to grow to womanhood she must be allowed to run freely in the open air; and from that time forward she followed her natural bent, spending most of her time out of doors with her father and her uncles on the farm. She rode the horses, drove the cows to pasture, and pitched hay. Two little stone posts marked the gateway of her own garden, which she made and tended. In after years she used to say that there was one form of farm work only which she had never done. To her great sorrow her mother would not permit her to milk the cows, for fear her hands would grow large and unbeautiful.

Mrs. Swallow, like her husband, had been educated at the academy in New Ipswich. Between her and her daughter there must have been a keen intellectual sympathy, for when in college Ellen painstakingly outlined for her mother at home books which she had read and lectures and sermons to which she had listened. But there was also a fundamental difference of opinion as to what came within a woman's sphere. In one of the letters written from college, Ellen told of an address made by a student on Founder's Day. This brought forth a vigorous protest from the mother, in spite of the fact that she had been assured that the audience consisted exclusively of faculty and fellow-students, and that the description of the youthful orator, "dressed in black with a lavender bow, her hair dressed plainly, and wearing white kid gloves," made a picture of pre-eminent feminine propriety.

Notwithstanding the fact that Ellen's predilections were for outdoor life and strenuous pursuits, household tasks were not neglected. By the age of thirteen she had, under the tutelage of her mother, mastered the housekeeping arts which in later years she valued so highly that she sought to have them embodied in the curricula of the schools. The sheets and pillowcases of a toy bed daintily hemstitched, a pair of silk stockings, and a beautifully embroidered handkerchief for which she took a prize at a country fair, when she was only thirteen years old, testified to her skill; while a china vase, which was a prize offered at the same fair for the best loaf of bread, bore silent witness to her early accomplishments as a cook.

Her father and mother, both well educated for the times, and both having been teachers, were extremely critical of the incumbents of the village school, and except upon rare occasions they instructed the child themselves. Her early years, therefore, were passed chiefly within her home, varied by occasional visits at the farm of her uncle, Stillman Swallow, in Nashua, whose daughter Annie was her most intimate associate during her girlhood and young womanhood. Here, besides enjoying the companionship of a large family of children, she took great delight in the high-bred horses with which the farm was stocked.

Her love of animals and her sympathy with them must have begun very early in life. In fact, some of the first outpourings of her generous and helpful spirit seem to have been toward pets. One of the products of her mother's skillful fingers were little white cotton rabbits, which found their way into many homes to the delight of children. When Ellen was four years old she broke her arm. After it had been put into splints, her mother found her out upon the grass one day, supporting herself upon her uninjured arm and painfully pulling grass for the cotton rabbits with the other.

Dunstable, during the time of Ellen Swallow's childhood, had a population of about five hundred and fifty, scattered over a territory of sixteen and a half miles, not more than one hundred of them living in the near-by village. It had no railway until 1850. Then the Worcester and Nashua cut across its western portion, but made no stop within the town. It was not until long after she left that railway connection was established with other parts of New England. In this isolated place she grew up, among an industrious and religious people. It was a fortunate childhood in many ways, for while her body was being gradually strengthened by out-of-door life, her mind was being stimulated by her home associations.

She was sixteen years old when her father sold his farm in Dunstable, and become the proprietor of the village store in Westford. A friend who knew her during the Westford years says that her young companions always considered her a member of the firm, so active was her interest and so unfailing the help which she gave her father. We may therefore consider the move from Dunstable to Westford to be the dividing line between a carefree childhood and a young womanhood of purposeful preparation for a life work toward which her steadfast gaze was always set, even when its outlines were least clearly defined.

The road from the Swallow farm to Westford led past the cluster of houses and the little church of the village of Dunstable, and passing through the pine woods suddenly came out upon an open space, across which one could see the academy on the high land at Westford. This was the road which Ellen Swallow traveled in April, 1859. With the strength and the courage of her fathers which had been bred in the stern realities of pioneer life, with their faith which had seen a beneficent Providence even in the rocks with which their paths had been strewn, and with a spirit tuned to the beauty of the quiet landscape and of the pines, she set forth, and as she traveled, suddenly the way opened before her, and there on the heights beyond she caught glimpses of opportunity.

Chapter II

GIRLHOOD

THE periods into which life naturally divides itself—those of preparation and education, of active labor, and of decline—are least clearly marked in lives of greatest power and most earnest purpose. For great power is likely to show itself in useful labor during the years which are usually given to education, and earnest purpose persists to the end, carrying with it the demand for continued training. Thus dividing lines are obscured.

If Ellen Swallow had been a person of only average energy and average strength of purpose, we might now be able to speak of her days at Westford as a period given to education, and to point to the places which were most intimately connected with her life there and say: "Here at the academy on the Common she was educated; there in the little store across the way her father worked to support his family and to educate his daughter; and there a short distance down the orchard-lined street, in the white house among the flowers, her mother made the family home." But so great was her energy and so independent her spirit, that she not only took an important part in the homemaking, but also insisted upon helping to raise the money for her own education. Naturally quicker than her father, and with a greater aptitude for the details of business, she became his constant assistant in the store. At the same time her mother and she, freed from the harder labor which farm life brings to women, found time from their housework to make the little home bud and blossom with the flowers of which they both were passionately fond. During the Westford period, therefore, she took a real part in the work which was going on about her, and was not removed from it for purposes of education. These years, instead of being given wholly to preparation, represent rather one stage of her developing power, one phase of the unfolding of a life in which labor and preparation for greater labor always went side by side.

Picking up the thread of her life at the time of its greatest complexity, when activity was greatest and interests most numerous, we are surprised to find how many of its strands may be traced back to childhood or girlhood. Of these the most persistent, that which stretched straightest and strongest from the beginning to the end and around which all other interests twined, was the love of home. To the separate household arts which she had learned to perfection during her childhood, she added in girlhood the art of household management, and during her mother's frequent sicknesses she had full charge of the home. She cooked, washed, ironed, cleaned house, papered rooms, and laid carpets. Those who heard her lecture in later years on subjects related to home-making, often took it for granted that, being a chemist, she spoke from theory and not from practical experience; but as a matter of fact there was no household task which she could not perform as well as anyone whom she employed. When she became an expert in an important branch of science, she added her knowledge of sanitation to skill in housekeeping, and brought both to the service of her home.

Closely connected with love of home was another interest which found its place almost as early in her life and also continued to the end. This was the passion for flowers which she shared with her mother. There are few letters from mother to daughter or from daughter to mother which do not contain some inquiry as to the welfare of the plants, some statement as to their progress, some hope expressed as to the blossoms to come, or some enumeration of blossoms which had already appeared. Friends at a distance, too, seem always to have thought of mother and daughter among their house plants or in the garden.

While still a girl she wrote to her cousin Annie:

"Please tell Lucy that my coliseum [ivy] has grown finely, has been in blossom ever since she was here. A few days ago I counted thirty blossoms and fifty buds. I will send a blossom if I don't forget it. I have made a basket for the ivy and hung it in the window. It has also been in blossom several weeks. I wish you could come and stay with me a few weeks; our bracing air would do you good. You have no idea how pretty our village looks in its summer dress. We have so many shade trees in the streets, and so many pretty orchards beside them, that at this time it is really a charming spot."

At a later time she wrote:

"The ivy that I had from your house covers the whole window and is in full bloom. It is the admiration of all. Our calla is magnificent; our Mobile amaryllis (we call it so in distinction from the common one because ours came from Mobile) is budded, and I expect will be well worth seeing. . . . I have a silver-leaf geranium about three inches high, which is budded. Won't it be a little darling? We have part of our plants in the store. People take so much notice of them that father is willing to have the trouble of them and has taken a great interest in taking care of them; has done more of it than he ever did before. I think he would rebel as strongly as any of us now to be deprived of them."

Beginning in girlhood too, and continuing as long as she lived, was a fondness for fiction, which was probably allied to her love of pleasant exploration and due to the eagerness with which her mind went out to every phase of life. She climbed with zest the difficult paths of science, but she also walked with pleasure the easier paths of romance. The friends of her busier years have a picture of her as, comfortably seating herself in a street car, she took a novel from her pocket or bag and became lost to the world about her; or as, the work of a long day over, she drew a footstool to a warm spot beside the fireplace or register and found in a story complete mental relaxation, which prepared the way for sound and restful slumber. It would be easy to think that this habit was acquired in the years of her greatest activity for the purpose of freeing herself at times from the pressure of care, but as a matter of fact it dated back to girlhood. Her uncle, George W. Taylor, after her death, wrote: "Ellen had become at about twelve years old a rapid reader, and was spending much of her time in reading works of fiction. I then said to her that I thought she better stop reading so much fiction and take up the study of more meritorious work."

That she had some misgivings herself is shown by a prim

little composition upon the subject of "Gathering Pebbles," which was written during her school life in Westford. After telling how she wandered for one whole afternoon by the seashore picking up stones, she adds: "Do not many people spend precious hours in gathering pebbles and only pebbles from other places than the seashore? When in our school days we idle away our time in all the various ways that only scholars can find, linger too long over some enchanting book, lay aside the textbook for the story because we do not feel like study, are we not simply gathering pebbles which look bright, but will fade when we look back in after years, and think how much more we might have accomplished?"

But the truth is that the reading of fiction never interfered with her other interests and pursuits, for she read with lightning rapidity, and could so sail off on the current of the story as to forget all her worries and return completely rested and ready for further work. And from no novel, not even one of small literary merit, did she ever fail to get some little suggestion which helped her to solve a practical problem, or some thought which could be woven into the philosophy of her life.

To the training she received in the store, which began with waiting on customers and gradually enlarged itself to include the keeping of accounts and the purchase of goods for which purpose she often made trips to Boston, as well as to her natural quickness of perception, may be traced the business ability which led to her being intrusted in her maturer years with large sums of money for all kinds of educational and philanthropic enterprises.

Life behind the counter, however, valuable as it doubtless was as a means of discipline and education, and important as its bearing was upon her later work, was not all roses. The store being of the kind known as a general store, she was obliged to sell tobacco, which she hated. It is said that at one time a group of men who had bought tobacco of her, filled and lighted their pipes in the store, seating themselves around the stove according to the usual custom. When the youthful storekeeper objected, they said, "Why do you sell us tobacco if you don't expect us to smoke it?" We sell you molasses, too," she replied quickly, "but we don't expect you to stay here and cook it up."

Two women customers, one of whom insisted upon having saleratus because she never could cook with soda, the other of whom demanded soda because saleratus did not make good biscuits, and who having been supplied from the same package were both satisfied and both confirmed in their original opinion, may have amused her at the time, but they probably inspired her with a desire to look more deeply into the nature of the things with which she was dealing, and may well have directed her thoughts toward scientific study.

Records of her life in Westford, though meager, show that her love of adventure was leading her into ever-widening circles of investigation. While in the academy, she spent her vacation with friends at Lynn who had a store from which they supplied groceries to the large houses at Nahant and elsewhere along the fashionable North Shore. While on these visits, it was her greatest delight to take her place upon the front seat of the delivery wagon, and, riding from house to house, learn "how the other half lived." The Ellen Swallow who as a girl widened her horizon by looking upon life from the front seat of a grocery wagon was the same person who, in after years, frequently left the more conventional routes of travel to explore the wilds of Canada in search of minerals, or to visit remote mining regions with her husband. She went to Europe, to be sure, in 1876, and again in 1884, but during the last twenty-six years of her life she preferred to go where daring feats of engineering were in progress, where mountains were being tunneled or rivers spanned, or where great, new cities were conquering unfavorable environments.

But her excursions to out-of-the-way places and into romance never, even in her youth, became purposeless wanderings, for the goal was always before her; and being determined to make her life count in some helpful way, she would return to the straight path she had marked out for herself and trudge bravely forward. Her earnestness and her deep faith, which in later years she trusted her deeds to reveal, found expression during her girlhood in the religious forms and phraseology of the day. "The extra dash of puritanism" which someone had said was added to her New England ancestry was apparent in the letters of this period.

"As it is Friday," she wrote in 1861 to her cousin Annie, "and I have a few moments which are not imperatively claimed, I take the opportunity to write the long-delayed answer to your welcome missive. I was disappointed, as well as you, at not being able to make my visit, for I had looked forward to much enjoyment from it; but Providence decreed otherwise, for wise reasons, doubtless. . . . I want to come and see you so much. I can see you all with the *mind's eye,* just as when I used to be with you, and even while I write your faces present themselves before me in various ways. I fancy myself again with you, out in the barn in the swing or jumping off the hay, and lastly husking corn, and anon up in your well-remembered room playing 'blindman's buff,' etc. . . . Ah! childhood's joyous days are fled, never more to return. God grant that our lives may be useful ones."

The education which she received at Westford Academy differed little from that given in the many other academies with which New England was at that time dotted. There was a little mathematics, a few compositions, some French, and much Latin. In the Latin she must have been thoroughly grounded, for her knowledge of it, and her ability to teach it, formed a capital from which she later received an income that made it possible for her to continue her own studies. She proved to be an excellent tutor, much in demand.

The successive principals of the academy, whose periods of service were measured by terms rather than years, and of whom there were four during her three years' attendance, were all Harvard graduates. The first was John D. Long, who afterwards became Governor of Massachusetts and later Secretary of the Navy. The second was Addison G. Smith, with whom she became well acquainted. After he left Westford they corresponded and exchanged books and views upon politics and literature up to the time of his death in 1874. This was the first of those comradeships with men which, added to the one great love of her life and to her friendships with women and her sympathy with children, made her human relationships peculiarly wide.

In March, 1862, she left the academy and was preparing to teach when the after effects of an attack of measles interfered with her plans. In May she wrote to her cousin:

"I am very glad the measles are over with, for I have dreaded them very much since I had the whooping cough, though it has sadly interefered with my plans for the summer, as I had engaged to try my skill in teaching the 'young ideas how to shoot.' It was a severe disappointment, but I feel it was all for the best. . . . I have not been obliged to lie abed a day before since I was seven years old, yet suffered less pain in the three weeks I was sick than in the same time for the last three years. I am gaining, though rather slowly, and am not very strong, as this writing will show."

In the spring of 1863 the family moved to Littleton, a town situated about three miles from Westford, where Mr. Swallow had bought a larger store for the purpose of extending his business. From Littleton the following letters were written to her cousin Annie:

LITTLETON, April 30, 1863.

"Are you surprised to see the new heading to my letter, or have you heard of our removal hither? Yes, we are really inhabitants of Littleton, or shall be when we have been here long enough. So you will never see our place in Westford in all its glory. Yet we have a pleasant place here, in some respects pleasanter than the other. The store is very large and nice. The tenement is not as convenient as one could wish, yet it is not very bad. It consists of a two-story ell containing two large rooms below and chambers above, with two rooms back of the store. Over the store is Central Hall. We have a large garden but no fruit trees. There is quite a little village, more, I should think, than at Westford. The house fronts upon a little common. When we get righted I think we shall feel quite contented. . . . I feel it my duty to stay at home under present circumstances instead of teaching, as I had hoped."

MARCH 22, 1864.

"Am going to teach this summer if it please God to grant me health and strength. School will begin about the first of May, and I shall be needed here to help take account of stock about the middle of April, so I shall have no time for visiting. I wish you could come and see me. I am going to the easterly part of the town, about two miles from here. It is a large school of some forty scholars. It will require a great deal of care and patience, but it is my chosen work."

JUNE 9, 1864.

"I have thirty-seven pupils. Am about two miles from home; go home every Friday night. I have a very pleasant boarding place, about as far from the schoolhouse as your barn is from the house. I have a few large scholars who study the higher branches, which makes it more pleasant for me."

SEPTEMBER, 1864.

"Thought perhaps you would like to know how I and my flock are prospering. Well, I guess about as well as could be expected. I have forty-one pupils and have to call out over thirty classes each day. You may judge there is some work in it. . . . I usually have to work harder Saturdays than any other day in the week. I have put up two wreaths of flowers since I was at Nashua, and have two in the house now to do. . . . Mother thinks it will be very lonesome here in the winter, so I have almost decided to remain at home, but cannot tell what may happen."

After this the work at home and in the store, and the care of her mother, who was often ill, took up so much of her time that she did not again attempt to teach. She wrote on February 10, 1865:

"I am the same Nellie as of old, full of business, never seeing a leisure hour, never finding time to study or read half as much as I want. . . . Father has a little extra business on hand now; is carrying goods to two villages in Westford; so I have to help him more. He has no one regularly now. Will have in the spring, probably."

It was during the intervals of time between teaching, storekeeping, and housekeeping that she prepared herself for college. There was an open book beside her, whatever she was doing. The winter of 1865-66 she spent at Worcester attending lectures and studying, though just where and whether or not for the distinct purpose of preparing herself for Vassar, which had opened a few months before, it has been impossible to discover. Here she practiced the strictest economy, living principally on bread and milk.

From Worcester she wrote as follows:

DECEMBER 18, 1865.

"It seemed real good to have one of your nice letters. I wanted to sit right down and answer it, but could not then, as I had a good deal to do before going home. I spent nearly a fortnight home at Thanksgiving. Have come back to spend the winter, if all is well. I enjoy the privileges I have here very much, and I have the opportunity of doing good, too, for Deacon Haywood has taken me to his Mission School and given me a class of bright little boys to look after. And I go with him to the jail sometimes, when there is need of missionary work."

APRIL 14, 1866.

"This is the anniversary of our beloved President's assassination. What gloomy days those were! I shall never, never forget that sad time. I think I could not suffer more than I did for two or three days, and if I could have foreseen all that has happened since, I think I should have almost lost faith even in God himself; yet I believe that all things will be ordered aright by the good Father in Heaven.

"I expect to remain in Worcester about two months longer, then if father is alone I shall probably go home, though I cannot tell what changes may occur ere that time; though there is no 'possibility' of your dreams proving true at present, for the young or old gentleman has not yet made his appearance who can entice me away from my free and independent life.

"I know of no lady with whom I would exchange places. The gentleman whom I think the most of and who comes the nearest my ideal in other things does not treat his wife as I wish to be treated; yet they are considered a very loving, happy couple, and are as much so as the average. I often tell him *we* could not live together more than a week if we were obliged to, though we agree very nicely now on most essential points.

"Oh! Annie, the silent misery I am discovering every now

and then among my friends whom I thought as happy as most, makes me shudder. Some things I learned yesterday about one of my dearest friends, made me almost vow I never would bind myself with the chains of matrimony. I don't believe girls usually get behind the scenes as much as I have, or they could not get up such an enthusiasm for married life.

"Annie, is it possible that we have attained the eventful age of twenty-three? Do you feel old? I am sure I don't, yet I have seen something of life in these years and it seems long to look back upon, and how little I have done for my Saviour in comparison with what I ought to have done. And now I fear I let many opportunities go by that I ought to improve. Pray for me, dear Annie, that my life may not be entirely in vain, that I may be of some use in this sinful world. I feel sometimes as though I would be glad to leave it, the ties that bind me to earth at times seem very slight."

There were love affairs at this time; the usual hopes and anticipations of young womanhood. After she had begun her work as a chemist, but before she became engaged to Professor Richards, she wrote to a college friend:

"I can now change the query, 'Will it pay to sacrifice love for fame?' into the declaration, 'It has paid so far;' " adding, "If I had not had an almost Napoleonic faith in my star I should have yielded." The star, if we may judge from after events, had no intention of guiding her away from matrimony, only of saving her from a marriage which, as a possibility, she could deliberately hold up before herself and compare with a career. Stars are not always leading us in the direction we think they are at the moment.

Having abandoned the thought of marriage, she bent her whole effort toward getting further education. At that day, however, there were few doors open to ambitious women. Until Wellesley and Smith were founded, about ten years later, New England had no college to which women were admitted, while Vassar, the woman's college just across the New York border, was so recently founded that its fame was just beginning to spread abroad. As there were no colleges in her neighborhood, there were, of course, no college preparatory courses. She herself had an honorable part in the work that led to the founding of the Girls' Latin School of Boston, in 1878.

Thus hampered and delayed in getting the education she desired, and with a feeling of power within her for which there was no outlet, she entered in 1866 upon the only unhappy period of her life. This unhappiness is not to be explained on the ground that she scorned the duties which lay near at hand, for she assumed her full share of work at home, in the store, in the church, and in the Sunday school. "Nellie was a very busy little woman," writes a friend, "and whether measuring off calico, weighing sugar, or acting as postmistress, she always had a kind and cheerful and helpful word. She was always studying up ways and means to better and improve things. She was not only influential in starting a reading and magazine club, but attended to all the details and pushed it through till the little post office looked a good deal like a periodical store." Whatever her hands found to do, she did. She cared for sick friends and neighbors; and in order to earn money, she sewed, and preserved flowers, organizing classes in this art.

Nor is there any evidence that her unhappiness was allowed to find outward expression. A man who, as a little boy, had known her during this period, wrote after her death: "She had an active part with the other young people of the town in the social life of the place, the fun and frolic that was going on, and she was a great favorite at our home. I vividly remember her presence with us as a nurse, a volunteer nurse, when we had serious sickness in the house. There were, of course, no trained nurses in those days, and in a country place like that no professional nurses at all. The neighbors used to help each other out, when there was severe sickness, by taking turns as 'watchers' with the sick. And the thing that impressed a very small boy about 'Nellie Swallow's' nursing—a thing that I have thought about hundreds of times since—was her wonderful cheerfulness and hopefulness when everybody else about the house was anxious and depressed. I can remember the sweet, encouraging tone of her voice and her winsome smile in those dark days."

But the tasks which were given her at this time were not

commensurate with her power, and the unused energy within her seems fairly to have turned upon her and to have reduced her almost to a condition of invalidism. It is difficult for those who knew the Mrs. Richards of later years, who, rising at half-past five, went briskly through a long day's work, scorning to rest or take naps, to believe that she was the same person who in 1868 wrote in her pocket diary:

January 6—Did not go to meeting, tired. *January 11*—Tired, indifferent. *January 20*—Tired. *January 27*—Tired. *February 1*—Busy, tired. *February 2*—Almost sick. *February 9*—Miserable, lay on sofa all day. *February 13*—Felt wretchedly all day. *February 14*—Lay down, sick. *February 19*—Oh! so tired. *February 23*—So tired. *March 20*—Tired. *March 24*—Tired. *April 11*—Terribly tired.

This was the story as she told it at the time. A few years later she wrote to a friend who found herself hedged in:

"I lived for over two years in *Purgatory* really, and I didn't know what to do, and it seemed best for me to just *stay* and *endure* and it seemed as though I should just go wild. I used to fret and fume—inside—so every day, and think I couldn't *live* so much longer. I was thwarted and hedged in on every side; it seemed as though God didn't help me a bit and man was doing his best against me and my own heart even turned traitor, and, well—altogether I had a sorry time of it."

But better times were coming for her. "One day she came up to my uncle's house," writes a friend, "and said: 'You know, Mr. Tuttle, that I have been to school a good deal, read quite a little, and so secured quite a little knowledge. Now I am going to Vassar College to get it straightened out and assimilated. What do you think of my plan?' "

The same little diary which contains the record of the suffering which she endured with outward calm contains the following entries:

September 15, 1868—Farewell to Littleton; met Father at Waldo House and took the Albany Express at 10.

September 16—From 5.25 to 10 in Albany. Arrived at Vassar, pleasantly welcomed, very tired.

September 17—First day at college; am delighted even beyond anticipations, the rest seems so refreshing.

Chapter III

AT COLLEGE

FORTUNATELY, at this point, Ellen Swallow takes up the story of her own life. During her years at college she wrote long letters, at least once a week, to her mother, which form an uninterrupted record, and which have come to be known as her *Vassar Diary*. Twenty-five years after she graduated, she heard some one say that it was unfortunate that the comments of students upon college conditions, which might be of value in determining college policies, were usually embodied in private family letters, and thus lost to the world. With her customary directness of action she sought out her own old letters and marked certain portions to be type-written, omitting the reference to purely personal and family matters, and also the long abstracts of books and sermons which she had made for her father and mother. Later she culled from the typewritten extracts all the passages which had special bearing upon the beginnings of Vassar, and published them in the *Vassar Miscellany* of January and February, 1896.

When she entered Vassar, in September, 1868, she was classified as a special student. Somewhat over a year later she was admitted to the senior class, and was graduated in 1870.

A college mate writes: "Her two years at Vassar belonged to the period when faculty and students alike (consciously or unconsciously) were forming the standards of the new college. Her part in the work was that of a strong personality, understanding well her own needs, and by the same light interpreting the needs of her fellow-students. Some years older than the average student, she was mature in character, with mental powers well-disciplined and controlled. To do work well for its own sake, not for its reflex on herself, she had already learned."

"While her primary purpose was study, she was alive to all

the best influences of college life, and in it she was an active though often silent force. To make the most of her own powers for the sake of using them in advancing knowledge and in broad and enlightened activity seemed to be her aim, while no opportunity for fellow service was to be let slip by the way. Independent in thought and action, quick to see far-reaching consequences, never self-assertive, she is to be counted among that strong company of the earlier students who while receiving much gave much to Vassar College."

The strongest personal influences which came to her in college were from Maria Mitchell, the astronomer, and from Professor C. A. Farrar, who was at the head of the Department of Natural Sciences and Mathematics. Miss Mitchell wanted to make an astronomer of her, and she would doubtless have succeeded if her science had not been so far removed from the earth and its needs. In the woefully brief autobiographical notes which Mrs. Richards left she said it was probably an unrecognized leaning towards social service which led her, an enthusiastic student of Maria Mitchell's, to abandon astronomy and study chemistry. Professor Farrar's very strong influence over her came partly from her respect for his ability as a scientist and a teacher, and partly from the fact that he took the very advanced position that science should help in the solution of practical problems.

Her natural bent was evidently towards scientific studies, for either in classroom or by examination she took all the courses in science then offered with the exception of one in mathematical astronomy, and wherever there was an opportunity she did additional volunteer work. One classmate writes that she was a member of a little group of three who in an elective course in chemistry analyzed everything that came in their way "from shoe-blacking to baking powder."

The selections from her letters which are given here and in Appendix A were made with a view to showing not only the external conditions of her life at this period, but also the pure joy with which she responded to the intellectual stimulus of her college life, which from the standpoint of biographical interest is quite as important. In many cases the references to her own progress and attainments seem egotistical, but it must be remembered that during those early days of pioneering she was almost like two persons, one of whom was making an interesting experiment and taking a step which was against all precedent and against the advice of all of her associates, while the other was a sympathetic onlooker, joyously recording successes. It should be remembered, also, that the letters were intended only for the eyes of a loving father and mother, who knew what sacrifices she had made, and who were, as a matter of course, to be told of any triumphs which she achieved.

VASSAR DIARY
1868-1869

September 10. The President admitted me to pursue the regular, or a special course. I was cordially welcomed by all whom I had met before (during the preliminary examinations in previous June)[1] and everything promised fair.

I had for dinner, soup, which was a fashionable one, water poured over meat, with macaroni a little larger than knitting needles, then roast beef, succotash, squash and potatoes, with rhubarb pie and canteloupes for dessert. All was nice as possible.

Our carpet is a little figure, red and green, bright and good. The walls are pure white, at least 13 feet high, the doors and casings, dark, the shutters, chairs and chamber set are chestnut, a black walnut whatnot, an oval study table, with a little waste paper basket underneath.

September 17. This morning I went over to the Observatory and looked through the telescope, an entrancing instrument. Had a very delightful call on Miss Mitchell and her father, who is a charming old gentleman. At eleven o'clock, we who had not been classified, went into the chapel to listen to Professor Hart for an hour. He accompanied Professor Agassiz to Brazil, and he told us stories of his adventures.

I do not feel the least anxiety now in regard to my studies. I do not expect to work much for a month.

. . . .

[1] The explanations in parentheses which are found all through the diary were made by Mrs. Richards in 1895.

The Art Gallery has about 600 pieces, some of them little gems and some are curiosities. The Library contains much of interest for me; history and travels and choice works which I have long wished to read. The table is well furnished with magazines. It will be a favorite resort to me.

September 19. I am so fortunate in my little family. All are studious and agreeable.

Some twenty or more of the girls wear their hair flowing to their waists without any attempt at doing it up. It is not usually curly, but long and straight. It seems as if they had had not yet dressed. . . . I hope you are feeling better by this time. I don't worry, because I can do no good by it. I left everything behind me at Worcester [about the time she went to Vassar her parents moved to Worcester] and live an entirely new life. Of course if you are sick or need me, you must send for me, and I will immediately come to you. Then will be soon enough to worry.

September 24. I have got so far settled that I will give you a sketch of my daily occupations. The bell strikes at six. At quarter of seven we have breakfast. Each one can leave the dining room as soon as she has finished, and thus I get time to make my bed, which is all we have to do in our rooms. In chapel we sing, and Miss Lyman offers prayer. We have ten minutes then for arranging our rooms, or, if it is done, for study, then we have twenty minutes alone for devotion and meditation in perfect quiet. Study hours do not begin until nine. At quarter of ten I go down to philosophy [physics]. I like Professor Farrar very much. There is an intellectual power about him. All recitations are forty minutes. At twelve we have Trigonometry, at one comes dinner, which occupies three-quarters of an hour, then I go out of doors for an hour, write an hour, and if my lessons are nearly ready for the next day, go into the Library directly after French, and perhaps read or study a little before dressing for tea, which is at six. Then chapel and another twenty minutes as silent time, from 7.30 to 9.45 for writing, reading, or study. I find I have much time to myself, and it seems so pleasant to be able to read and write with much comfort and without danger of interruption, which used to disturb me so much. I have not been homesick for a moment. I have nothing to complain of. The Faculty have not reached S(wallow) yet, so I do not know what studies I shall take in addition.

It would seem that there was an immense amount of travel in this great building, but on counting up, I find that my regular work requires my going up and down about two hundred and fifty steps daily, and I have to walk nearly a mile on the corridors.

Miss Lyman said yesterday, "You know people will persist in calling this a school, when it is not a school at all, but a college really." She also said, "The Faculty do not consider it a mere experiment any longer that girls can be educated as well as boys."

I am very glad that I did not come earlier for they have made great improvements, and I think now is just the time to commence with the new rules.

October 4. We of this parlor get on harmoniously. I am quite well and perfectly contented. We have festooned clematis all about the room, and have a new tablecloth, black and green. We had all the long morning to ourselves until half past three, which is the regular hour for service. We listened to a very dull sermon from a Poughkeepsie clergyman. I do not wonder some of the girls dread Sunday, which hardly seems a Sabbath to me, save in the rest from study. I shall go down to the city whenever it is pleasant. We have just been to our usual corridor prayer meeting, a half hour together every Sabbath evening.

The only trouble here is they won't let us study enough. They are so afraid we shall break down and you know the reputation of the College is at stake, for the question is, can girls get a college degree without injuring their health?

I am not working hard at all in my classes. My regular studies do not take quite all my time, so that I have time to read and study other things. It is wonderful how all my wishes are granted without my asking or working for it.

October 15. We have a sheet of paper with our six names written at intervals of a few lines, headed "Slang," pasted on our parlor door and every time one of us uses a slang phrase or a bad word, as "goodness" we have to write it down and pay a penny besides. When we get pennies enough, we will have a treat. The girls are afraid they will not get many pennies from me. I have not been caught yet.

October 18. Miss Lyman had some beautiful thoughts beautifully expressed this morning, on Economy, taking God's greatest example and trying to impress it upon us that we were each one his stewards. Dr. —— gave us a sermon of over an hour's length this afternoon, on "Sin exceeding sinful." It was good enough, but he might have said it all in half an hour and it would have done the girls more good. . . . We have so many religious exercises on Sunday, prayers and silent time. Our corridor prayer meetings make more than most people get and some girls are holding a daily prayer meeting. I think it is too much.

October 19. I have taken my first lesson in riding horseback. I rode a little black pony, Josephine. [The only extras on her college bill for the first year were for riding lessons.]

October 25. Our Bible classes were organized this morning and I was assigned just where I had hoped, to Prof. Farrar. He is such a large-souled, noble man and deep thinker. We are to study church history which will just suit me.

November 6. I have been very busy all the week. Have been perfect in all my lessons. We are just through our examinations in philosophy. I have not failed in any of them. I am very well. We had chicken pie for dinner and pumpkin pie and cheese yesterday for dessert, but I do want some mince pies and pork!

November 13. I was so vexed yesterday morning that I did not think of meteors and that Miss Mitchell did not tell us. The girls who watched on the Observatory counted 3500.

I must tell you that we had rules for table etiquette read in our corridor meeting to-day. Never put a knife in the mouth. Never eat anything with a knife that you can eat with a fork. Eat soup noiselessly from the side of the spoon.

November 25. I cannot risk my health without having a rest (at Christmas). The twenty-six weeks that follow in one unbroken line will be hard enough with all the strength that I can lay up. I came here wholly unfit for study and my first care was to look after my body, as my health is the first importance. Having got that in pretty good condition, I gave my brain the lead . . . working every moment of the time, even carrying the train of thought to the dinner table, which is not allowable, always aspiring to the first place. I have a double incentive now, for I have fully decided to remain here one and very likely two years longer, and upon my standing now will in a measure depend the employment I shall have. I think there will be no difficulty in arranging matters satisfactorily and I must keep the body in good condition to do the bidding of the spirit. We live so isolated and so unanxious a life here that a change is indispensable, to me at least, and if I choose to dress more simply and use the dollars in other ways, I feel justified in so doing.

My ivy is the pride of the third corridor north.

November 26. Miss Lyman sent for me the other morning to say that I was accepted for a scholarship and that she had no doubt I would make good use of it.

December 3. This has been quite a pleasant day for me. I have been promoted in German, so shall have to study a little harder, but it will be very nice.

Don't do anything for my coming home, only have some mince pies. I shall be hungry as a bear. I have gained thirteen pounds since I came.

January 20, 1869. I had a German letter to write for Miss Kapp yesterday instead of a lesson. I put it in rhyme, twenty-four lines in German, ten syllables in a line. I have to read an essay before our Literary Chapter to-morrow night. It is not written, only stray sentences, and one for the Natural History Society on Saturday, not even touched. We are to commence a drill review in Chemistry to-day which takes much time and I have to give all my strength and courage to comfort Miss ———, who gets so tired and discouraged.

January 23. I am enjoying our philosophy now very much. We have been making the universe to-day by a large globe of oil in alcohol and water, throwing off planets, etc.

February 5. As the half year closes on Tuesday next and many studies are finished, there has been a deal of reviewing and examinations which makes hard work. My being promoted in German made my work double and I wanted to keep up my reputation in mathematics. I think of what you say in regard to doing extra in order to keep the standard people set for you, because you have excelled in some things, but while I am so well and can study nine hours a day without a headache, I am all right.

February 16. I fear you will get more than you are thankful for this time. If my notes are not quite plain enough to be interesting, say so. If you are really pleased, I like to do it for you, for it takes much reading to cull the grains of wheat from the chaff and writing them down aids in fixing them in memory. (This refers to the abundant extracts and abstracts which fill the letters.) . . . A letter of eighteen pages is something I never wrote before.

February 19. Last night Miss Mitchell gave her maiden lecture before Chapter Delta. I was invited and I enjoyed it so much. She was rather timid and would not allow any of the Faculty admitted, but it was charming to hear her talk of the people she had met when in Europe and she need not have feared. Her manner was very simple and correct without any pretension. She stipulated that she should sit at a table and she gave us sometimes her notes taken at different times, and sometimes she spoke her thoughts. We all came away more proud of her than before, if that was possible. She spoke of Caroline Herschel who aided her brother so much in his discoveries and Mrs. Somerville, whom she had the pleasure of visiting when about eighty years old, and who "came tripping into the room" to meet her. Also she told us of Harriet Hosmer. She urged us to do our work well and faithfully. She said that living a little apart as she did, she could see our advantages better than we could.

February 28. Last night's lecture did not come up to my expectations. Prof. —— is a learned man doubtless, but I did not think he understood what to say to us. I expected something new and worth knowing, not to be told that the rocks lay in beds and that the continent was not in its present shape in the beginning, and that when pebbles rubbed against each other they wore off into sand.

March 18. This morning Miss Lyman gave us a regular "dressing down." She said that we should look as though we were interested, if we were not, when we went to lectures, and that we should give close attention to whomever was speaking. She remarked that Prof. —— was a distinguished man and if he should go to Europe, all the learned men would flock to hear him; that he had made many discoveries and was speaking on his own ground and was capable of teaching wiser people than any of us are. Very true, but he would not speak to such a company of learned men as he spoke to us. (This refers to the talking down to our supposed level which most of the early lecturers were guilty of.) Miss Lyman was quite shocked that two or three ladies actually carried work into the chapel. I should like to have heard Miss Lyman talk to three hundred young men in that strain.

Easter Sunday. One morning this week Miss Lyman sent for me. I immediately began counting up my sins, as we all do when that message comes to us. I concluded I had not done anything but what I could brave her wrath for, so I marched into the dreaded little office with good courage. She was exceedingly pleasant and wished to know if I could find time to teach two young ladies arithmetic. I could, of course, and she said I might try and that Prof. Farrar would give me the necessary directions. Each will pay about $5.00 a month. [From this time on, until her education was finished, she supported herself, chiefly by tutoring. She had come to college with $300, partly saved and partly borrowed, and she had expected to remain one year only. Her entire expenses during her first year at Vassar were $515, of which $400 was for tuition and board. She spent in the summer of 1869 $66.50, which brought her expenses from September, 1868, to September, 1869, up to $581.50.]

April 20. A party of Juniors and others planned an excursion to the Cannon Factory at West Point, to go down on the boat and back at night. Prof. Farrar and Miss Braislin were to go as leaders. Miss Lyman "could not think of it" and wondered they had not asked her before the plan was made. They told her they had no doubt she would let them go. Then they asked her to see the President about it. She said she would do so, but he would first ask her what she thought and she would tell him she could not consent. He might do what he pleased. "It might get into the papers" and that would never do. It must not happen on account of the precedent it would set. "It was not because it was West Point" oh no! "It was the principle of the thing." It seemed a real insult to Prof. Farrar. He was justly very indignant. It is a pretty idea. If we are to be educated so that we can speak in public or to be self-sufficient anywhere, we ought to be capable of taking a little trip without fearing a notice in the papers. Just at present the whole faculty is in disgrace with us.

[Forty-one years afterwards, Mrs. Richards, speaking at an alumnæ luncheon, referred to this affair: "Shall we ever forget the West Point expedition which did not take place? Now we know that rapid growth is cancerous or fungoid and that it was not so much fear of us individually as of what our development meant in the future that led to the tantalizing caution so galling to us."]

Tell father he must not think it hard to work. Work is a sovereign remedy for all ills and a man who loves to work will never be unhappy.

April 29. Founder's Day exercises opened with music on the organ. Dr. Raymond offered prayer, then a poem was read by the composer, one of the students, then Miss Whitney gave the address. She is a tall, commanding looking girl, not handsome, but intellectual. She was dressed in black silk with a lavender bow. She had a long watch chain about her neck. Her hair was arranged plainly and she wore white kid gloves. She was a good representative of Vassar. The gestures were admirable and the voice good. There is little that could possibly have been bettered in words or ideas.

Friday afternoon we went out surveying, took about half our measurements. I intend to draw a map of the farm. It will make me hurried, but then I am used to that.

May 10. I laughed at your reference to our training. Why, little mother, you used to keep posted on the world's progress. If women are to vote, they ought to be able to state their reasons for thinking in a certain manner on the subject. I hope they will be able to use language better than most of the men and not make such a fuss about speaking in public. I do not care to have women vote, but they will do it, in my opinion, while you are living and they ought to be prepared for it, but that is not the aim of the work here. We only do our own talking. We read our own essays and of course we ought to be able to give our sisters our ideas. Miss Whitney was speaking to us, not to a public audience. The place was proper and fitting for her. No one but a student was fitted to give a eulogy on our benefactor.

And as to surveying it is light work compared with washing. The chain is light and clean and the pins also. The instrument for taking observations can be easily carried and it is very fine work to take bearings. We cross brooks and woodlands for pleasure and pray why not for business? It requires a good deal of skill to go over a fence or a wall built of such small shaly stones as the walls here, but it can be done and it is an accomplishment. I do not mean to do it with long dresses and hoop skirt, of course not. I find nothing in it not consistent with grace or virtue. I prefer surveying for a week to spending a week in fashionable society even of the best class and there would be far less danger. Tell Merrick that when I come home I will be ready to go out with him and test my capability. Anything that will take the American woman out of doors will be a blessing to her.

Miss Lyman gave the girls a lecture on working in the garden. She said that some of the finest ladies she knew took the charge of both the vegetable garden and the flowers and raked and did the weeding. At first she was shocked to see the ladies in Canada working out of doors but she found that they were better and healthier and she got over her prejudices. I think you will have to make up your mind to do the same.

May 16. We have very much more than usual to do this week. In calculus Prof. Farrar is anxious to accomplish an immense amount of work in this first class in college. We have a lesson of ten pages for to-morrow. The class of '70 will be the first under the new system and will be the best trained of any, so we have some ambition. I am really astonished at the amount of work we do. I think few men in college do as much as we do here.

It is not orthodox to be found outside the grounds except in parties of three, so that if one is hurt, one can stay by to see that she does not elope and one can run to get help. Accidents so often happen to girls walking quietly in the road, that this is of great consequence! !

People have a curiosity to know what monstrosity is to arise from my ashes, do they? I feel much like saying, confound their base ideas of true education. But I will only say, tell all such interested individuals that my aim is now, as it has been for the past ten years, to make myself a true woman, one worthy of the name, and one who will unshrinkingly follow the path which God marks out, one whose aim is to do all of the good she can in the world and not to be one of the delicate little dolls or the silly fools who make up the bulk of American women, slaves to society and fashion. I do not intend to ever say anything in reply to the half sarcastic inquiries and covert sneers I have heard so much from those who think that a person must have a profession if she has been to college. College is a place to learn. When you find what stuff you are made of, then is the time to choose and study a profession, if ever. I only say this to quiet your sensitive nerves and to give you a weapon with which to defend your pride. I do not wish any defense for myself.

1869-1870

September 21. It is so good to get back to studying.

Wednesday. I spoke with the President yesterday concerning my studies for the next semester. Shall re-read Wayland's Moral Science and he will examine me. Then I shall take political economy and physiology thus completing the whole curriculum, excepting Greek, and a year each of French and Latin.

Wednesday. What think you? The senior class must read their compositions on the platform in public! We are horror stricken. Miss Morse sent for me and wished to have me take an oversight of a little friend of hers who has trouble with her Latin, so that brings in a little pin money.

October 17. (Contains an account of the trip to Rondout by the geological class.) This is the first day I ever wore my gymnastic suit all day long. I hope it will help bring the day when such suits will be worn. It is so suitable. I wonder if the Poughkeepsie Journal will chronicle the wonderful sight. We have often ridden through town but never walked their streets before.

October 20. Our first hour in the laboratory. Prof. Farrar encourages us to be very thorough there, as the profession of an analytical chemist is very profitable and means very nice and delicate work fitted for ladies' hands. I also made my first observation of the sun, which I shall keep up every day at noon. There were only three little spots to-day.

October 26. I spent nearly an hour in the observatory last night looking through the telescope. It was a new experience and a delightful one. I saw considerable, though Miss Mitchell said I must not expect to do much the first night. I thought Jupiter and his moons were magnificent through the little telescope, but Miss Mitchell let me look through the large one, the third in size in the country, afterwards, and it was beyond description. The round planet with its beautiful colored light, and so close to it the bright moons. To-day the sun is very turbulent. The spots that have been quiet for four days have disappeared and changed greatly. Last night the aurora was wonderfully beautiful.

We are to have three lectures on Egypt by Dr. Thompson. I expect they will be treats.

October 30. I wonder if it is because I am doing more good that I enjoy so much more than last year. I thought then that nothing could be better than to see and hear so much of value, but last night, after our natural history meeting, where Prof. Orton told us seven what we might do for science, thinking of that and of my astronomy and chemistry and of the world whose door is now wide open to me, I felt as though I could never murmur at anything again, but could be useful and contented in learning, any where that I might be. I feel as though I was fast on my way to the third heaven, if not already there. I do not wonder at the enthusiasm of an Agassiz or a Livingstone.

November 7. My life is becoming very busy, as it always does. The old woman's prophecy is surely being fulfilled. (Referring to the meeting in Lowell of a person who stopped me on the street and said "And you have a great deal of work to do.")

The first of importance to tell you is that on Thursday I found the nebula that I found the week before. Miss Mitchell was very much pleased and said that I showed a facility with instruments and with my eyes that promised well. I do not know yet if it is a real discovery or if some one had seen it before. Miss Mitchell does not know it. I shall be much hurried this week and next on account of the meteors. . . . I must sleep on Saturday and Sunday as much as possible as Miss Mitchell needs six or seven of us with her Saturday and Sunday nights, and there are few girls who are able to do it.

November 14. On Friday night I determined to wake up at three in the morning. I did it within three minutes. It was quite clear and I went into the Lithological cabinet on this floor, perched up in the window and watched for meteors. I saw eight in an hour, two very fine ones. Last night was very dubious, but two of the advanced class, the only post-graduate, and myself went to the observatory at ten o'clock. It was quite an honor that Miss Mitchell chose me of all her class of fourteen to be her aid. She ordered Miss B. and myself to lie on the lounges in her sitting room. We were not to raise our heads, or speak if Miss Mitchell came in to look at instruments, unless she called us. It cleared up at quarter of eleven, the stars came out quite bright. One very brilliant meteor flashed through the haze in the north. I was the only one at the observatory who saw that, for I had drawn the lounge to the east window where I could see clearly. In ten minutes it was cloudy again. Miss Mitchell said it was one of the darkest nights that she ever knew. At five we went sound asleep and slept until half past six. So ended our famous meteor night.

The first two of the senior essays were read last night. The Faculty freely and without demur or condition admitted me to the class of '70 last night and highly complimented me on my meekness and patience in quietly waiting these six weeks.

1870

March 20. *"Es bildet ein Talent sich in der Stille, sich ein Charakter in dem Strom der Welt."* So says Goethe, and I've been making a talent here in the quiet of my life, as I couldn't if I had entered into the rushing, foaming stream that flows even here. I had been in the hurrying waters too long not to appreciate an opportunity to lie on the bank and rest, watch others, and gain strength for the coming years. Moreover, I am a thorough-bred democrat, clear to the marrow, as perhaps you have reason to know, and there is too much of aristocracy and particularly monarchy, in the air of the College for me to safely pass freely about, without coming into collision with, when there would be great danger of an explosion. I early learned where the powder magazines were situated, and carefully avoided the vicinity, but did not put out my candle, and now I begin to see that my little light has had its effect. An extra covering is thrown over the fiery material when I am around, so that I can come nearer, and I feel that I've conquered.

Again, time is too precious to me to waste in chitchat and gossip. I worked too hard for the opportunity of being in Vassar College to throw away any of it. Very few people pay well in intellectual or moral coin for the time spent, therefore, the greatest misfortune to me would have been popularity at first.

The two happy years at Vassar were brought to a close by a botanical expedition to the Catskills in company with a party of college friends. The last entries in her diary are:

Wednesday, June 15. Rose at 3½, walked to the station. Went to Mountain House. *Thursday.* Explored. *Friday.* Came back. Successful trip. *Monday.* Mother came. *Tuesday.* Class Day. All went well. *Wednesday.* Commencement. A.B. Said goodby. All kind. *Friday.* Home.

Chapter IV

STUDENT OF CHEMISTRY

THE Massachusetts Institute of Technology, founded for the purpose of offering advanced instruction in science and opportunity for research, and of making a connection between science and the industrial arts, was opened to students in the year 1865, the same year that Vassar was opened. Up to the year 1871, its students were all men. In January of that year, a woman was admitted as a special student in chemistry. On the morning of her entrance, she had an interview with the president, Dr. J. D. Runkle, who, having worked valiantly for her admission, was from the first deeply interested in her success. He introduced her to the only other woman in the building, Mrs. E. A. Stinson, the assistant in charge of the chemical storeroom, and asked that arrangements be made for her comfort. Later in the day, when passing the storeroom, he inquired of Mrs. Stinson how the young woman was getting on. "She looks rather frail to take such a difficult course," Mrs. Stinson said. "But did you notice her eyes?" was his reply. "They are steadfast and they are courageous. She will not fail."

The new student with courage in her eyes was Ellen Swallow, who seven months before had been graduated from Vassar College. The story of how she succeeded in becoming the first woman to enter the Institute of Technology, or, for that matter, the first woman to enter any such strictly scientific school in the United States, makes an important chapter in the history of woman's education.

When she left college there was little to determine her future course except a leaning towards science and a need for self-support. Like most educated women of her day she turned to teaching as a means of livelihood. Unlike most of them, however, she thought of any teaching she might at this time do as only a steppingstone to more advanced work. With her eager desire for wider experience, she seems not to have considered any position short of California, and finally decided upon South America. At the time of her graduation she was under appointment to go in the autumn to the Argentine Republic, as one of six teachers engaged by President Sarmiento. But the Argentine Republic was at that time in a state of war, and during the summer conditions became so unsettled that the government was obliged to break its contract with the teachers from the United States.

The final word concerning the change of plan did not reach Miss Swallow until late in the summer. In the meantime she watched and waited. On August 21 she wrote to a friend, "I do want to go if it is best, but I am afraid that selfish ambition is too much at the root of my desire for it to be granted."

She did not, however, content herself with watching and waiting; she worked also. The first three weeks after her return from college she describes as "one grand Aunt Dinah's clarin' up time." Her mother had been sick all winter, and the work had run behind. She set about, therefore, not only cleaning house, but also getting her own and her mother's wardrobes into shape. According to a letter written on July 26, she got out all her trunks, boxes, and bureau drawers; she sorted, mended, washed, and ironed, and arranged all her worldly possessions for the summer. She papered her room, made "a nice toilet stand out of two empty tea chests, a piece of heavy bedspread and some white fringe," took up and put down entry carpets and other carpets; took up and set out plants; ripped up dresses, washed, turned them, and made them over. To this long recital of activities she added, "So you may imagine I have not had time to be very misanthropic," and "I take books from the library to read when I sit down for a few minutes to cool off."

"Don't you see," she wrote later to a friend whose plans were also unsettled, "how wisely our different natures have been provided for during these weeks? You need some outside aid to quell your inward disquiet, and you've had it under circumstances calculated to draw your thoughts from yourself. I, always self-reliant, have had to fight my battles alone and unaided. I have those around me who look to me for help in their trials, never dreaming that I have any."

The South American plan having failed, she apparently

decided to take a little leisure in which to meditate upon what
to do next.   On September 15, she started upon a three
weeks' trip to Nashua, Dunstable, Westford, and Littleton. "I
went to my birthplace," she wrote on October 8. "Saw great
trees planted by my hand, great boys nearly six feet high
whom I had rocked in the cradle, and felt the wrinkles
deepen and the *old* in my joints at the sight. I visited new
households formed since my last visit some four years ago,
and found babies in abundance. I liked my new cousins and
thought the world would be peopled without my troubling
myself in the matter. . . . I went to Littleton and saw the dear
faces and was welcomed most heartily.

"Well, here I am," she continued, "no nearer my winter's
work than when I left you, to any earthly eye. I have tried
several doors and they won't open. I am not discouraged or
blue at all. I've full faith that the right thing will come in
time. I've only to work and wait. I've lived in the greatest
calmness all summer, not feeling the old unrest and fretting
against the fetters, and I know the blessing of contentment.

"I wonder if there would be any chance for me to take
private pupils in Latin in the Western cities. I think I would
do it though I believe I would go into a chemist's shop in
preference. Does Dayton boast any drug stores or the like?
Would it be advisable for me to advertise, think you, for a
situation in such a place? I rather want to dip into some
science.

"I often feel as if I must have something good in store for
me so many people give expressions of confidence in my
future—never a croaking word do I get. I hope I shall not
neglect the right thing when it comes, but I begin to feel
anxious to see something done. I can't lie idle and must stir
in some direction."

On the day after this letter was written, she must have
decided in what direction to stir, for she wrote to Merrick
and Gray, commercial chemists in Boston, asking them if
they would take her as an apprentice. Her final decision to
study chemistry was probably reached through a desire to
help her father in the new business upon which he had
entered, that of manufacturing building stone. She wrote to
commercial chemists because no school then open to women

offered more chemistry than she had had at Vassar. Merrick and Gray replied that they were not in a position to take pupils, and that her best course was to try to enter the Institute of Technology of Boston as a student—a most extraordinary piece of advice to be given to a woman in 1870. She realized that if she acted upon it she must do so unaided, with no support or encouragement from her friends.

"There's no sense in going further—it's the edge of cultivation,"

they said to her in effect. But she decided that the time had come for the "edge of cultivation" to be pushed a little further forward, and wrote at once to the Institute of Technology, asking if the school admitted women, and giving as references Maria Mitchell and Professor Farrar. To this letter she received no answer for four weeks. In the meantime she wrote to Booth and Garrett, of Philadelphia, another firm of chemists. These good Quaker gentlemen replied, on November 14, that they were not in need of any assistance, for "experiment, study and reflection" were their sole occupations, and that these could be performed only by themselves. They regretted that they knew of no position to which they could direct her attention, although they had "heard that female assistance had been employed in the apothecary store." They regretted the more that they could render her no aid as they desired "to see proper means of livelihood thrown open to females."

The sympathetic spirit of this reply led her to write again, urging her case. Their second letter stated that they would take pupils only upon the payment of $500 a year, which of course, in her self-dependent position, put the thought of study with them beyond the realm of possibility. Like Merrick and Gray, they advised her to try to enter a scientific school.

In the time that elapsed between writing to the Institute and receiving a reply, she wrote the following to a friend: "I have quite made up my mind to try Chemistry for a life study and have been trying to find a suitable opportunity to attempt it. I've been busy with this and hoped to have something to report, but everything seems to stop short at some blank wall and I suppose I'm like Baalam and don't see the angel of the

Lord in the way. . . . I trust something will come to pass soon for I fear I shall get impatient.

"I've been making some lovely wax flowers for a lady to give as a wedding present and some for our Fair, also sewing for the Fair and helping make fancy things, doing a little in that way, reading some and cooking, Thanksgiving, etc., going to lectures, etc., etc. I've been full of business and it is well, else I should go wild over all the hindrances I find in my path."

Ten years later she wrote to a woman who had consulted her about preparation for a definite line of work:

"I know just how you feel; you want your own work to do in the world. You want to feel that just a little is your own. Is not that it? Well, I went through a good many years of that. After I felt the power to do I could not sit and fold my hands. I have found my work and plenty of it, but it is not what I had planned it to be and it did not come to me until I was nearly thirty years old."

On the twenty-eighth anniversary of her birth, December 3, 1870, the Faculty of the Institute of Technology formally received her application for admission, which had been in the hands of the secretary, Dr. Samuel Kneeland, up to that date. It voted, however, "to postpone the question of the admission of female students until the next meeting." On December 10, "the question of the admission of Miss Swallow was resumed and after some discussion it was voted that the Faculty recommend to the Corporation the admission of Miss Swallow as a special student in Chemistry." That same day, however, it was "*Resolved* That the Faculty are of the opinion that the admission of women as special students is as yet in the nature of an experiment, that each application should be acted on upon its own merits, and that no general action or change of the former policy of the Institute is at present expedient."

It was on December 14 that President Runkle, who had previously said to her that he considered the introduction of ladies to the Institute "a consummation devoutly to be wished," wrote her as follows:

"*Dear Miss Swallow:* The Secretary of the Institute, Dr. Kneeland, will notify you of the action of the corporation in your case at a meeting held this day. I congratulate you and every earnest woman upon the result. Can you come to Boston before many days and see me? I will say now that you shall have any and all advantages which the Institute has to offer without charge of any kind. I have the pleasure of knowing both Miss Mitchell and Mr. Farrar of Vassar. Hoping soon to have the pleasure of seeing you, I am

Faithfully yours,

J. D. RUNKLE,

President of the Institute."

So it came about that the answer to her question, "Are women admitted?" was not "*They* are," but "*You* are." To the clause in President Runkle's letter, "without charge of any kind," Miss Swallow afterwards referred, saying: "I thought it was out of the goodness of his heart because I was a poor girl with my way to make that he remitted the fee, but I learned later it was because he could say I was not a student, should any of the trustees or students make a fuss about my presence. Had I realized upon what basis I was taken, I would not have gone." Fortunately she did not know.

Just before she received word of the success of her plan, she had engaged to work in a store for the two weeks preceding Christmas. This delayed her entrance to the Institute a short time, but it gave her something quite as valuable to her as two weeks of study—an understanding of what the Christmas rush means to the shopgirl. Christmas Eve she worked until half-past ten without supper.

On Christmas she wrote to a friend: "I would give very much to have an hour's talk with you on the prospect the future is opening to me. I want your opinion on it and the support of your interest in what lies before me. Very mysteriously God leads us, doesn't he? He grants us our wishes, often tho in different ways from what we expect. You will know that one of my delights is to do something that no one else ever did. I have the chance of doing what no woman ever did and the glimpse I get of what is held out to me makes me sober and thoughtful, not that I want to turn back but I fear that I can't carry steadily all the load I've taken and feel inclined to go slowly at first, not with my usual dash. To be the first woman to enter the Massachusetts Institute of Technology, and so far as I know, *any scientific* school, and to do it by myself alone, unaided, to be welcomed most cordially, is this not honor enough for the first six months of post-collegiate life?"

Shortly after the holidays she went to Boston and engaged a room at 523 Columbus Avenue. This was a boarding house kept by Mrs. Blodgett, the mother of Isa Blodgett, her most intimate friend at Westford Academy. She could not, however, afford to pay for board, and so she and her friend Helen Morse, who roomed with her, boarded themselves.

Established in Boston, she entered upon the same program of work and study which she had followed all her life. As early as January 26, she had assumed temporary charge of the office of a friend in his absence from the city, and was "enjoying being in the office and the Institute also." Shortly afterwards she took full charge of the boarding house in which she was living, during the absence of Mrs. Blodgett, whose daughter was critically ill. She kept peace in the kitchen, directed the servants, planned the meals, and took care that the routine of the house should not be interrupted. "I got up at half past five this morning," she wrote at this time, "to get Mr. Blodgett his breakfast because he had to get away on the early train and I was afraid the girls would forget." In the meantime she was carrying on her work at the Institute, and was supporting herself by tutoring.

Having been admitted to the Institute as a special privilege, she set about making herself indispensable. "I hope in a quiet way," she wrote on February 11, 1871, "I am winning a way which others will keep open. Perhaps the fact that I am not a Radical or a believer in the all powerful ballot for women to right her wrongs and that I do not scorn womanly duties, but claim it as a privilege to clean up and sort of supervise the room and sew things, etc., is winning me stronger allies than anything else. Even Prof. A. accords me his sanction when I sew his papers or tie up a sore finger or dust the table, etc. Last night Prof. B. found me useful to mend *his suspenders* which had come to grief, much to the amusement of young Mr. C. I try to keep all sorts of such things as needles, thread, pins, scissors, etc., round and they are getting to come to me for everything they want and they almost always find it and as Prof.—said the other day—"When we are in doubt about anything we always go to Miss Swallow." They leave messages with me and come to expect me to know where everything and everybody is—so you see I am useful in a decidedly general way— so they can't say *study* spoils me for anything else. I think I am making as good progress as anyone in my study too— They say I am going ahead because Prof. Ordway trusts me to do his work for him which he never did anybody else— the dear good man—I am only too happy to do anything for him." (Professor Ordway had a large practice as consulting expert in technical chemistry.)

"They are even daring to joke a little. The other day I found a letter on my desk there with the A.B. crossed out and A.O.M. written. What do you suppose they meant? I couldn't get it from them. Prof. Ordway whom I privately consulted said it must be Artium Omnium Magistra. I interpreted it *old maid*."

Mrs. Stinson, who became her faithful friend and ally, and who was "happy if she could just hear her voice," told many stories of her helpfulness during these early days. One of these stories would have shocked Mrs. Richards herself in later days when she was advocating scientific methods of cleaning, but it shows how quick she was to see and to meet a need. One day a professor of Chemistry was preparing for a lecture in a room which had not been swept or made ready for the class. Shortly before the time of the lecture the janitor entered, but detecting an odor like that of rotten eggs, due to the escape of sulphuretted hydrogen gas, he fled precipitately and refused to return. What was to be done? The class would be in in a few moments and the room was still unswept. Recognizing the emergency, Miss Swallow seized a broom, and starting at one end of the room while Mrs. Stinson started at the other, they had it swept before the class arrived.

To understand the difficulties which Ellen Swallow overcame during that first year in order to hold to the course she had laid out for herself, one must know something of her home life. Early in March her father was struck by an engine in the Union Station at Worcester and so badly injured that he died four days later. She wrote on April 30 to Mrs. Hughes: . . . "I was sick about the first of March and came up here for a few days. While here, just able to lie round on the sofa, word was brought to us one morning that father who had left home an hour before was being brought home, his right arm crushed by the cars.

"Oh, Flora, imagine if you can the horrible scene—the amputation, the terrible agony he suffered 'in the arm that is gone,' the anxious watching and care which all came upon me, as he looked to no one else, trusted all in my hands, night and day for four days, a few hours' delirium, then sleep, and a glorious awaking in Heaven.

"I had strength to go thro all, calm, cheerful, without a tear, but it almost took reason, when the strain was removed, and I've not recovered yet. I sometimes fear I shall give up before the spring is thro. So many things I have to do which almost kill me, business which calls him up to me, seeing people who want to talk of him, and yet I will not allow myself to shirk. I could not leave mother alone tho it is torture for me to be here and so I go back and forth to Boston every day. I have tried thro April and shall one month more—then the Institute closes and I hope to go back to Boston in September to live. Mother will still live here. I am succeeding quite well in my work and the future looks well. What special mission is God preparing me for? Cutting off all earthly ties and isolating me as it were."

A few months later she wrote to a friend who was in trouble: ". . . When you feel an indication of a certain morbid feeling resolutely set your mind in another direction, and don't give up easily. Let the mind know there is a will power to control it in a measure. This is possible. I never could have lived thro these sad months if I had for an instant allowed my mind to dwell on the terrible scenes of my father's death. I turn my attention by *something* and so successfully that I've not dreamed of him as crushed or dead but once and that was a few nights ago after sitting here mending a dress all the evening and thinking of things at home. Now when the thought comes to my mind I shut the door tight and run to the other side and take a book or pencil or plan something for the future and so turn the attention which is a very child to please—so easily is it diverted."

Thus during the last few months of that first year of her work at the Institute she was supporting herself, was settling her father's estate, and was making daily a trip to Boston and back, which even in these days of rapid transit takes more than an hour each way. And yet, in spite of the shock, the sorrow, the worry, and the weariness, she held her place in the Institute, keeping the door open for other women.

Chapter V

IN THE LABORATORY

THE next four years, from 1871 to 1875, were spent by Miss Swallow at the Institute of Technology, first as student, then as student assistant, and finally as assistant in the chemical laboratories. If these years were to be considered only as they offered opportunity for self-expression, the record might be made up from her letters, for she repeatedly wrote of pleasure in her work, of satisfaction that she was able to "do real things of value to people," and of pride that "her opinion was getting to be of consequence on chemical analysis." But during this period, as at previous times in her life, preparation for work and work itself overlapped, and her student labors gradually took the form of professional services in sanitary chemistry. It seems best, therefore, to connect these years with that part of her subsequent life which was given to systematic scientific work, even though this may somewhat disturb the sequence of the narrative. Such a treatment has another advantage also, for it is only against the background of her scientific labors that her other varied and ever-changing activities can be seen in their true proportions.

Mrs. Richards' public activities, numerous as they were, fall rather naturally into two groups, those of leadership and those of expert service in sanitary science. To compare these two kinds of work, and to try to say of one or of the other that it was her greater contribution to the life of her times, would be idle; and to seem to be making such comparison, or to be laying undue emphasis upon one or the other, would be unfortunate. Yet in the written record it is almost inevitable that the work which she did as leader should loom larger and more prominent than the other. For so multiform were the activities of this kind, so wide the territory over which they carried her, and so many the people with whom they brought her in contact, that they must necessarily form a large part of any written record of her life. It is well, there-

47

fore, to see them against the background of that patient work which she did day after day and year after year, in the quiet of her laboratory and classroom. And all the more so because those who were closest to her feel that the authority with which she spoke on matters of public interest and her very wide influence were due to the fact that she had painstakingly made herself master of a certain field, restricted though it may be considered. An eminent chemist who heard her speak upon a platform with several other women expressed this idea when he said that her speech carried more weight than the others because she was herself a *Fachmann,* her training and her work being behind every word which she spoke.

Considering the service which she was destined to render in the line of public health and the training of sanitary chemists and engineers, the time of her entrance into the Institute was most opportune. On April 16, 1869, less than two years before she began her work, the Massachusetts legislature had passed an Act providing for the establishment of a State Board of Health. This board, to which Mrs. Richards gave some of the best working years of her life, became a leader in the public health movement of America. In its first report, its general principles of action were set forth in the following words: "No board of health, if it rightly perform its duty, can separate the physical from the moral and intellectual natures of man. These three qualities of man are really indissoluble, and mutually act and react upon each other. Any influence exerted to the injury of one, inevitably, though perhaps very indirectly, injures another. As in the physical world there is a correlation of forces, so that no force is ever lost but only interchanged with another, so do these various powers and qualities of man act upon each other, and act and are acted on by the physical forces of nature that surround him." We may well believe that this statement and the plea which follows for an ethical purpose in public health work met a responsive chord in the soul of the woman who during her college life had said, "I must keep the body in good condition to do the bidding of the spirit."

Very soon after the organization of the State Board, the question of the pollution of streams by industrial establishments and by the sewage of towns was brought to its attention, and it decided to investigate the matter, selecting Professor William R. Nichols, of the Institute of Technology, to make the chemical analyses. Water analysis being at that time a new branch of chemistry, Professor Nichols wisely decided to begin by a very thorough examination of the waters of a limited district, and chose Mystic Pond for this intensive study. He began his work in April 1870, and made his report in September of the same year. As a result of the conditions shown, the legislature issued an order in April 1872, instructing the Board of Health to make an extensive inquiry into matters connected with sewerage and water supply. In doing this it followed the example of England, whose Rivers Pollution Commission had made its first report in 1870. In undertaking this larger task, the Board again intrusted the chemical work to Professor Nichols, and this time he chose Miss Swallow as his assistant. "He thus availed himself," to use Miss Swallow's own words, "of the technical skill of hand gained in using instruments of precision under the tutelage of Maria Mitchell." This was doubtless the work to which she referred in a letter dated August 14, 1872: "Now a new work has been put into my hands which will tell, and that by a Professor who does not believe in women's education." In November of the same year she wrote: "The record since I wrote might almost be summed up in one word 'Work.' I have made about 100 water analyses and that is only part of my daily duties. I have been studying with the classes since October 9th. I have to prepare my lessons evenings."

While this work was going on, Professor Nichols was making frequent trips to England and to the Continent in order to learn what was being done abroad, and during his absence was directing the work of the laboratory by correspondence. In writing of him after his death, Mrs. Richards said: "He accepted nothing short of absolute accuracy, as if under oath. Each new assistant was put through a vigorous process of testing as to the accuracy of work no matter at what cost of time and money." Miss Swallow, as Professor Nichols' pupil and assistant, therefore had the advantage not only of being in touch with some of the most advanced work in sanitation which was being done in the world, but also of having a most rigorous training for the part which she was to take in later work. In his report made to the Board in 1874, Professor Nichols said: "Most of the analytical work has been performed by Miss Ellen H. Swallow, A.M., under my direction. I take pleasure in acknowledging my indebtedness to her valuable assistance and expressing my confidence in the accuracy of the results obtained."

Her student life at the Institute, through good fortune as to the time when it began and the men with whom it brought her in contact, led toward what was probably the greatest direct contribution of her life to public health—her part in the extensive sanitary survey of the waters of the state, which began in 1887. This work was great in its conception and great in its consequences. The survey itself lasted for nearly two years, and consisted in monthly analyses of samples from all parts of the state, representing the water supply of eighty-two per cent of the population.

Before this survey began, a separate laboratory for sanitary chemistry had been established at the Institute of Technology, the first of its kind in the world. This laboratory, which was opened in 1884, was in charge of Professor Nichols, with Mrs. Richards as an assistant. Professor Nichols died in 1886 and Dr. Thomas M. Drown was appointed his successor. Dr. Drown planned the great survey and placed Mrs. Richards in charge of the laboratory and of the corps of assistant chemists. After the completion of the investigation many problems were left to be solved, and Dr. Drown and Mrs. Richards remained in charge of the water laboratory of the state until it was transferred to the State House in 1897.

In a work of this magnitude, it will be seen that the success depended very largely upon system and regularity in the management of the laboratory. The samples were collected and transported at large expense. Upon their arrival at the laboratory it was necessary to examine them within a few hours or they became useless. If a sample was spoiled by delay it was not replaced, and in order that there might be no gaps in the record, Mrs. Richards worked not only all day, but frequently late into the night, and on Sundays and holidays. "I have been *under water* since June 1 of last year," she wrote in March 1888, to a friend, "and I suppose it will be the same another year. We are testing all the public supplies once a month and we are up to 2,500 samples already. I am on constant duty from 8 o'clock to 5.30 or 6 every day, Saturday included."

In a letter written in 1904, she referred to the strain of this work, saying: "I worked fourteen hours a day on five and sometimes seven days of the week. If the day was too hot for analyzing water the work was done at night." In the course of this investigation more than forty thousand samples of water were analyzed, either wholly or in part by her. During all this time laboratory and experimental methods were being perfected and new forms of apparatus devised. In the splendid co-operation which brought the survey to a successful issue, there was little thought of where the credit for specific parts of the work lay, but it is recognized that, as Dr. Drown said in his report to the Board, "the accuracy of the work and the no less important accuracy of the records were mainly due to Mrs. Richards' great zeal and vigilance."

The very large number of analyses, showing as they did the condition of the water of all parts of the state at all times of the year, were in themselves a valuable record, and made possible many important generalizations. One of these found expression in what is known as the Normal Chlorine Map, which has become a model wherever sanitary surveys are being made. Upon this map all the places whose natural unpolluted waters contain the same amount of chlorine were connected by lines very much after the fashion in which places with the same barometric pressure are connected in a weather map. To these lines the name of *isochlors* was given. When the map was completed, it was discovered that the isochlors ran in a general way parallel to the line of the seashore, and that the distances between them and the shore corresponded very closely with differences in the amount of normal chlorine present, thus revealing the fact that for all places the same distance from the sea the chlorine in the natural waters might be considered the same. By means of this map, it is possible with very little trouble to tell of a given place in Massachusetts (except of places on Cape Cod, which is washed on all sides by the sea) how much of the chlorine found in its waters is due to its nearness to the sea, and how much is due to pollution. This suggested to other states and countries that there might be a like uniformity in the chlorine content of their waters, and consequently served as a valuable starting point for the examination of waters in many parts of the world.

As in the case of the work of general water analysis for the state, so in the case of the making of the chlorine map, it was a great piece of work to which a large number of faithful workers contributed. Whether the important deduction from the large number of figures at hand first occurred to Mrs. Richards or to some one else, no one seems to know, but one thing may be said, if it had not been for the vast number of reliable figures which had been secured through her generalship and her management of the laboratory, the chlorine map would never have been made.

In 1873 Miss Swallow received the degree of Bachelor of Science (in Chemistry) from the Institute of Technology, becoming its first woman graduate. The same year she received the Master's degree from Vassar upon the presentation of a thesis and after a long and searching examination. At this time she hoped to go on with investigational work and to secure a Doctor's degree. But while there were many to make use of her skill as an analyst, there were few to realize what the opportunity to do original work would mean to her, and there were few to encourage her and help her to surmount the difficulties which at that time lay in the way of a woman's securing such an honor.

In spite of the fact that the times were against her, she traveled far enough in independent work to look over into the promised land that only those may enter who make contributions to knowledge. In 1872 she came into possession of a small piece of a rare mineral, samarskite, which others had analyzed without discovering anything unusual about it. After analyzing it with great care, she reported in a paper published by the Boston Society of Natural History that there was an insoluble residue which could not be accounted for. To those who were working with her in the laboratory she repeatedly said that she believed it to contain elements not then known. A few years later two new elements, samarium and gadolinium, were isolated from this mineral.

After her first experience as water analyst under Professor Nichols, Miss Swallow entered upon a large private practice in sanitary chemistry, including the examination not only of water, but also of air and of food, and the testing of wallpapers and fabrics for arsenic. In 1878 and 1879 she examined a large number of staple groceries for the state, the results of her investigation being published in the first annual report of the Board of Health, Lunacy and Charity, which had succeeded the earlier Board of Health.

Her work as an expert in sanitary chemistry constituted a most important and at the same time a unique form of public service, even when it was done for fees. But frequently she chose to give her expert knowledge without remuneration. For example, a friend might be choosing a site for a country home or a camp or a summer cottage. Mrs. Richards' contribution, or shall we say her part of the housewarming, would almost invariably be a thorough investigation of the water supply. When we consider how many people fell victims to typhoid fever during their summer outings, we realize how valuable this contribution was. Or the question of the water supply for a school would arise. Mrs. Richards was always ready to offer her services without cost, if she felt that the enterprise was in a struggling financial condition or if she had a personal interest in it. As alumna trustee of Vassar she performed invaluable services in testing the drinking water of the college, in order to determine the efficiency of a sewage disposal plant which had been installed. The half of what she did to protect human life from the danger of impure waters will never be known by any one person, and for that reason its complete story can never be written.

During the time that Miss Swallow was studying at the Institute, she was assistant not only to Professor Nichols, but also to Professor Ordway, whose specialty was industrial chemistry and who carried on a large amount of work as consulting expert for various manufacturing establishments. It was through her association with him that she was appointed, in 1884, chemist for the Manufacturers' Mutual Fire Insurance Company. In this capacity she did much valuable work bearing upon the danger from spontaneous combustion of various oils in commercial use. This was pioneer work, and it is said that in the course of it Mrs. Richards often prophesied that the time would come when every material used in building would be thoroughly tested. The great underwriters' laboratories of today show that she had true prophetic vision.

It was in the course of her work on oils that she became acquainted with Edward Atkinson, economist and philanthropist, who invented the Aladdin Oven and with whom she later worked out many problems in the application of heat to food materials under a grant from the Elizabeth Thompson Fund. For him, too, she evolved several methods of determining the impurities in lubricating oils, with special reference to cottonseed oil, and devised what was known as the "evaporation test" for non-lubricating volatile matters. She also made an investigation of the possibilities of recovering wool grease which attracted world-wide attention, and a study of the composition of cottonseed hulls which proved of great commercial value. In 1877 she devised a new method for determining the amount of nickel in various ores, and as a result she became an authority on the subject and frequently acted as referee on disputed points.

It was her special joy to be chosen to help those in the business world whose faces she believed to be turned toward a future of better living conditions. She was keenly in sympathy with certain progressive commercial enterprises started by college women in later years, such as the Sunshine Laundry of Brookline and the Laboratory Kitchen of Boston. Shortly before her death, Mrs. Richards gave a course of lectures to the employees of the Laboratory Kitchen upon the relation of personal cleanliness to safe food.

Not the least important of Mrs. Richards' chemical work was that which she did in connection with Professor Richards' researches. She spent the summers of 1881 and 1882 with him in the copper regions of Northern Michigan, where he was making investigations into methods of concentrating and smelting copper. During these summers she acted as his chemist, and Professor Richards says that her extreme accuracy and wonderful promptness contributed largely to the value of the experiments.

In 1876 she became instructor in the Woman's Laboratory connected with the Institute, whose history will be told in a later chapter. In 1884 she was appointed Instructor in Sanitary Chemistry in the Institute of Technology itself, a position which she filled until the time of her death. During the twenty-seven years in which she was in charge of this laboratory, she trained a large number of young men, who went out to every part of the United States and to many foreign countries to take charge of similar laboratories. It was for her classes in Sanitary Chemistry that she wrote "Air, Water and Food," with the co-operation of Assistant Professor A. G. Woodman.

In 1890 there was inaugurated at the Institute of Technology the first systematic and comprehensive course in Sanitary Engineering to be established in any seat of learning in the world. Much of the prestige of this course is undoubtedly due directly to Mrs. Richards' labors, wise advice, and co-operation. In the training of the engineers, Mrs. Richards, who, as one of her associates has said, would probably have been an engineer herself if she had been a man, always took a very prominent part and a special pride and joy. Her particular field of instruction was in sanitary water and sewage analysis and their interpretation, and in air analysis, which was of peculiar value to engineering students specializing in ventilating work.

The laboratory of Sanitary Chemistry has often been called unique because of the exceptional completeness with which it was equipped, but it was unique even more in this, that there went forth from it workers not only thoroughly acquainted with the technique of water and air analysis, but also inspired with the desire to serve their fellowmen. The facts of science were never to Mrs. Richards, nor to those of her students who caught her spirit, mere facts; they were above all the possible vehicles of social service. She sent forth from her laboratory and classroom "missionaries to a suffering humanity."

Chapter VI

IN HER HOME

DURING the four years of her student life at the Institute of Technology, Miss Swallow continued to live at 523 Columbus Avenue. At first she "boarded herself," for economy's sake, but as her income from chemical work increased she was able to pay for board as well as for her room, and living became less of a struggle. She was able also to contribute to her mother's support. "I have been fixing up Mother's house for her comfort," we find in her letter of November 17, 1872, "as she has to do without me. I go up once in two or three weeks to spend a night and that is all. She will have to pay a heavy assessment on insurance of her house on account of this great fire, and I may need to do more for her. I have been having $60 a month besides my evening classes and so could take care of myself, but I can't tell how the spring will find me." "I have settled the house upon her," she had written earlier, "and she has the life insurance besides, so she will not want. I have the amount invested in the stone speculation which may bring me 5 or 10 thousand or not a cent."

The fire to which she referred was the great Boston fire of November 1872. This she described in a letter to a friend with the terseness and vividness which were characteristic of her literary expression: "It was a strange feeling to stand out in the still night and see so intense and angry a monster eating up our stone walls." It was characteristic of her also that after a few days, having reflected that the loss was exclusively in material things, she should have written: "It was only property that was destroyed, and mainly the kind of merchandise that we put on our bodies, so we can do with less and not suffer. We ought to realize that as the Lord's stewards we ought not to wear all that He gives us to spend for His poor and needy."

Out of the money which her father had invested in artificial stone, and which she hoped to recover, she used often to build, not air castles, but artificial stone castles. "More than anything that has occurred for a long time," she wrote in November 1871, to a friend who was in trouble, "your letter made me wish that my 'Frear-Artificial Stone' house was built (it is to be out here on Huntington Avenue—which at present is under several feet of Back Bay water) and in running order. Then there would be a warm corner and good chance for you, and no end of bugs and minerals close by. I would gather a houseful of my wayworn friends and we'd have such a gay old *home* of it. But there would be plenty of *work* if I was round. You know me well enough to believe that."

But the stone house did not materialize, and the home she made after her marriage and in which for thirty-six years her wayworn friends found rest and refreshment for the soul as well as for the body, and which more than any other one place they associate with her, was not on Huntington Avenue, but in Jamaica Plain, a beautiful subdivision of Boston.

On June 4, 1875, Miss Swallow was married to Professor Robert Hallowell Richards, head of the department of mining engineering in the Massachusetts Institute of Technology. "Your Professor," she had called him in her letters to her mother, following a pretty way she had of putting the good things of life away from herself with a little mental shove, as if of course they rightly belonged to someone more worthy. Miss Swallow and Professor Richards, differing widely in temperament, she being quick to see, to move, and to act, he slow, deliberate, and judicial in his mental attitude, had met upon the common ground of interest in scientific pursuits and had fallen in love with each other. "Cupid had appeared among the retorts and receivers," as Miss Swallow's facetious friend, Mr. Smith, expressed it.

Professor Richards was born on August 26, 1844, in Gardiner, Maine, the son of Francis Richards and Anne Hallowell Gardiner. The families from which he is descended, the Richardses, the Gardiners, the Hallowells, and the Tudors, have all been prominent and have played an important part in the life of their times. The Richards family had at the time of Professor Richards' marriage been connected with the famous Howe family through the marriage of Professor Richards' brother, Henry Richards, to Laura Elizabeth Howe, daughter of Samuel Gridley Howe and Julia Ward Howe.

The sons of the Richards family had been classically educated as a matter of course, and there was no thought that Robert would be an exception. For seven years, five of which were spent in England and two in the United States, an effort was made to force him into the mold which such a training offers, the only results being anxiety to his friends and suffering for himself. In February 1865, while at Phillips Exeter Academy studying Latin and Greek and looking forward to the Harvard entrance examinations, he received a letter from his mother in Boston, saying that her cousin by marriage, Professor William Barton Rogers, was about to start a scientific school, and that perhaps he might want to enter it instead of Harvard. Professor Richards said later that he hoped he had politeness enough to say good-by to his headmaster, but he was not at all sure, and that if he did it was the only formality to which he gave time before leaving for Boston. Arrived there he immediately entered the Institute of Technology, being the seventh pupil to matriculate. Admitted to classes in geology and chemistry, and being encouraged to relate what he had learned to the life about him, the scales fell from his eyes, and for the first time in all his life he said he *"saw."* Like Miss Swallow he had reached his lifework through tribulation of spirit, though the tribulation had been of a different sort from hers.

Before Professor Richards and Miss Swallow were married, they had selected a home at 32 Eliot Street, Jamaica Plain, about four miles from the Institute. To this house they went directly after a quiet wedding in Union Chapel, a mission church with which Miss Swallow had connected herself. To the young married people who lose their heads more or less on their wedding day, it will be comforting to know that even the staid professor and his learned wife made something of a muddle of their preparations. "Robert made several blunders in packing his things," his wife wrote the day after the wedding, "and when he got here he found he had no necktie but a white one. Before I had done laughing at him, I found that I had left all my keys in the closet door at 523

Columbus Avenue, and could get at no clothes except those I had on." So the professor had to go in town wearing his wedding necktie and get the keys which would release his wife's workaday clothes.

On June 7 they started upon a unique wedding trip to Nova Scotia, accompanied by Professor Richards' entire class in mining engineering, which he was taking out for practical work. On their return, a Vassar friend who was accompanied by some fashionable women, strangers to Mrs. Richards, happened to meet her on the steps of the Institute. The strangers refused to believe that the woman in outing costume, which included heavy boots and a short skirt, much less familiar then than now, was in reality a bride, just returned from her wedding trip.

The details of the housekeeping of the woman who organized the American Home Economics Association, and who succeeded in making a home and carrying on a profession at the same time, are, of course, of general interest. This fact gives an excuse for piercing the veil of privacy that hangs about the home, and for asking what manner of housekeeper Mrs. Richards was and how she ordered her home life.

In general, it may be said that her home was not strikingly or obtrusively different from any other well-conducted home, the differences which existed being in the amount of attention given to the essentials, in its cleanness—which was of the shining order so far as surfaces were concerned and which extended to hidden places and even to the air, clean air being her hobby—in its freedom from fads, and in the intelligence with which it welcomed any new household utensil or furnishings or practice which gave promise of contributing to health and efficiency. When Mrs. Richards began housekeeping in the seventies, she furnished her house with carpets as everyone else did. But when for the sake of greater convenience or safety she changed her methods; when, for example, she substituted rugs for carpets, began to use gas instead of coal for cooking, installed a telephone, or experimented with the vacuum cleaner for house cleaning, she always counted the cost, not only in money, but in time and steps. When she began to use a gas stove she had a meter placed in her kitchen, and with the assistance of a young engineer who was living in her home made a thorough study of the amount of gas required for preparing different dishes and for carrying on various household processes. She carefully computed, too, the amount of time involved in caring for rugs and hardwood floors as compared with carpets. In her last public address, which was at Ford Hall, Boston, on the subject, "Is the Increased Cost of Living a Sign of Social Advance?" and in which she reviewed her housekeeping experiences of thirty-five years, showing that the cost had doubled in that time, she gave abundant proof that she understood her own problems, not only in their relation to her family life, but also in their social bearings.

When Professor and Mrs. Richards went to housekeeping, Jamaica Plain was connected with Boston by a very slow, one-track street railway and by a steam railway whose station was about three-quarters of a mile from the house. They made a sacrifice of time, therefore, in order to live in a place where they could have a detached house and a garden. A house with a roof of its own unconnected with other roofs Mrs. Richards always considered essential to the best family life. Their house on a corner lot on a diagonal had air and light on all sides and also sun.

In 1883 a small Sanitary Science Club was formed in Boston in connection with the newly organized Association of Collegiate Alumnæ. Each member of the club made a study of her own home, and in addition Mrs. Richards threw open her home for a study by the entire club. She often said laughingly, afterwards, that that study cost her five hundred dollars because of the changes which it led her to make. One permanent result of the work of this club was a little book, "Home Sanitation," edited by Mrs. Richards and Miss Marion Talbot, one of the most helpful features of which was a series of illuminating questions which the housewife might put to herself with reference to her home. This was only one of the many cases in which Mrs. Richards put into permanent and available form work which other people allow to be lost to the world.

In the summer of 1908 I was visiting at her house when she received from Professor John R. Commons an advance copy of his Score Card for Houses, with a request that she criticize it. She handed it to me and asked me to score her own house; and having made the necessary examination and measurements, I had the pleasure of handing it back to her with a perfect score marked upon it.

The following prosaic details are given because there are young people all over the country who have looked to Mrs. Richards for guidance in small matters as well as in large, and who will value more minute particulars.

The house was heated by a furnace and ventilated by means of a skylight in the third-floor hall, which was kept open except in the most inclement weather, thus insuring the passage of clean, fresh air, even when the windows were closed. The extra fuel which this involved was not considered a luxury but a necessity. In places where the air was peculiarly liable to pollution there were extra provisions for ventilation. In the kitchen, there was not only a hood over the gas stove, and screens in the tops of the windows so that they could be lowered as well as raised, but also two holes cut in the very top outer walls and fitted with registers which could be opened or closed by means of cords. There was a similar ventilator at the highest point on the back staircase which led up to a back hall separated from the rest of the house by a door. Thus any odors which escaped from the kitchen when the door into the stairway was open found an easy means of escape. The fireplace in the living room had a drop for the ashes which led into a closely bricked compartment in the cellar. Many years ago, when most people were going without hot water when there was no fire in the kitchen stove, Mrs. Richards installed a small heater in the basement for summer use and a water back in the furnace for winter.

Over the chandelier in the study, where the most gas was burned for illuminating purposes, there was a ventilator designed by Professor and Mrs. Richards. It consisted of a cylinder with three branches, one over each burner. The main pipe or cylinder was carried through the ceiling, then through the beams and side walls of the house to the attic, where it was connected with the chimney. This carried off the products of combustion and also acted as a ventilator.

There were no curtains in the house, with the exception of short washable ones in the bedrooms and bathroom, but many of the windows were full of plants and vines. Shortly after Professor and Mrs. Richards moved into the house, they enlarged the dining room, making a place for plants at the back which served the purposes of a conservatory, but which because of its accessibility was much more practicable for a home where little help was employed. This extension, which looked toward the southwest, was supplied with a water tap so arranged that the plants could be sprinkled by means of a hose without danger of injuring any of the furnishings of the room. No draperies ever gave to a room the beauty which Mrs. Richards' flowers gave to her dining room.

The food served at Mrs. Richards' dining table was always determined with reference to its effect upon efficiency in work. If after a fair trial a given food seemed to leave the brain dull and the body unfit for labor, it was rejected. This process of elimination disposed, in the course of time, of most of what are known as "made dishes." There were few rich gravies in her bills of fare, few complicated salads, and little pastry. The bills of fare were made up chiefly of meat, which, however, she never used in very large quantities, of good homemade bread, fruit, and vegetables. Fruit or simple ice cream usually constituted the dessert. As time went on and life grew complicated, Mrs. Richards was forced to adopt what she considered unnecessary elaborations, but her ideal was always simplicity.

Established in their new home, Mrs. Richards decided not to pass the housework over to the usual hired helper, but to make a home for girls who were anxious to get an education and to allow them to work for their board. For several years this arrangement continued, until the pressure of outside work made it necessary for her to have regular help. During all this time, however, she had the additional assistance of a little girl who came at first to help after school, and later was sent by Mrs. Richards to cooking school and became so expert that she took full charge of the housekeeping. When she was married, in 1884, Mrs. Richards, instead of mourning over her loss, rejoiced that she had had a part in the training of a good homemaker. As Professor Richards once said, after telling me that they had found it somewhat expensive to help students by giving them work at their home and in their offices and laboratories, "But we decided that that was *what we were here for.*"

"Yes, I think my housekeeping is a success," we find in a letter of March 11, 1878. "My first young woman is now in Smith College by its means. I have six in the family this winter. My mother has come to live with us and I have two young women paying their way both here and in the Laboratory. The result is that we are doing good and the cost of housekeeping is not a mere outgo. We have pleasant people around us and willing hands and quick brains for any emergency."

Mrs. Richards' second regular helper came to her in 1884 and stayed with her almost continuously for twenty-six years. After she had been there about ten years, a terrible tragedy left her and her mother the only members of their family. Mrs. Richards immediately took the mother into her home and gave her the room which had formerly been occupied by her own mother, who had died a short time before.

In the autumn of 1910, when it became necessary for Mrs. Richards to make a new arrangement for her housework, her skillful management became very apparent. Having selected two new girls, she put into their hands typewritten directions, telling them where to find things, where to order things, and where to telephone in case of emergencies of various kinds— accidents to plumbing, for example. She made note of the regular engagements of the family, the general character of the meals which she wished to have served, and other details of this kind. The most interesting fact about these directions is that they embodied just enough information to keep the household running smoothly until the girls could adjust themselves to their new surroundings, but not enough particulars to be confusing. No wonder that a graduate of the Institute of Technology, who had lived for a year in Mrs. Richards' family, wrote of her recently: "She had mastered the principles of scientific management long before they became the subject of discussion in the industrial world."

One of the characteristic features of her housekeeping was the regular weekly program which she laid out and which contributed very greatly to the economy not only of her own but of other people's time. Tuesday afternoon she always remained at home. In the intervals between calls she brought her housekeeping up to date and made plans for the coming week. On that evening, Professor Richards' brother, George H. Richards, who lived in Boston, always dined at the house. This insured a weekly visit with him without the necessity for correspondence or arrangement of dates. If there were dinner parties, they were always arranged for Tuesday night. Monday evenings for a great many years were regularly given to an uncle of Professor Richards, Richard Sullivan, who was an invalid and finally became blind. He, like Mrs. Richards herself, was interested in the progress of science. She read to him popular treatises on science, periodicals, and books of travel. This engagement she never broke during all the years of his invalidism. If she were out of town, she wrote to him a long letter on Monday evening, telling him of her work and her plans. Her devotion to "Uncle Richard" makes a beautiful chapter of her life and one with which few people are acquainted.

About twenty years after her marriage, she so far overcame the Puritan prejudices of her early years as to become interested in the theater, and Friday evenings were given by her and Professor Richards to this form of entertainment. Their friends knew that they would be going to the theater on that evening, and frequently arranged to take seats near them in order to get the opportunity for a short visit.

Not only were the weeks carefully planned for, but also the days. Each night she wrote out brief notes of the different things to be done the next day, and the order in which they were to be taken up.

No description of Mrs. Richards' home life is complete without an account of the help which she constantly gave to Professor Richards in his professional work. It was his somewhat unusual task to develop a department of mining engineering many miles away from any of the mines. This task he performed so successfully as to make his department one of the strongest in the country, and in the upbuilding of the work he had not only her sympathy but her active help. Her quickness in reading extended to other languages than

English, and by following foreign journals and books she was
of invaluable assistance to him.

Mrs. Richards' skillful planning of her days and hours left
time for abundant hospitality. This hospitality, as it went out
to friends from out of town, was quite her own. She never gave
up her regular work for them, but always had them on her
mind, and seemed to know by intuition just what each particular person would want to see in Boston and just how to
direct him or her so as to economize time. Those who experienced this hospitality of hers often remembered the little
maps which she used to draw for their convenience. These
maps were like her handwriting. They had just enough lines
on them to serve their purpose, but not one to spare. In
making them, as in forming a word, she knew what could
be left out as well as what must be put in.

But there were those who shared in the hospitality of this
home in more intimate ways. One of them, a niece of
Professor Richards, says: "The hospitality of her home was
literally unbounded. This kind door was *always* open. No
piled-up amount of work, no complication of engagements,
interfered with the welcome that was always shining and
ready. Think what it is to be able to say of a house that
there one felt that one could never come at the wrong time
or be in the way! Such hospitality is hard enough to accomplish in one of the great modern country houses, with endless
guest rooms and a host of servants; but here more often than
not the guest, without ever knowing it, had the hostess' room.
I have known her, at the time of a family reunion, to fill
every room in the house with relatives. 'They can all see
each other more comfortably here, and some of them might
find the expenses of a hotel difficult to meet,' she would say.
After a merry evening, she would bid them a smiling good-
night, slip in town herself for a bed at the College Club or
elsewhere, and be back in time to greet her happy and un-
conscious guests at breakfast.

"I think that to every one who had the privilege of knowing her in her own house, the thought of her brings with it,
as a matter of course, a picture of that house. It was an
expression of herself, and it is hard to find words to express
at all adequately the sense of restfulness, of peace, which

seemed a part of it. It was like breathing clearer air to come
to it. The dust of non-essentials had been swept away; and
not only this, but the life-giving supply of oxygen seemed
greater here than elsewhere, and one breathed an air at once
restful and invigorating. Persons leading perforce a complex
city life, beset with undertakings overtaxing time and strength,
came here as to a refuge, not only for dear affection, but
for refreshment and rest—for actual strength. No house of
leisure that I know gave the sense of quiet and tranquillity
that this house of keen and arduous work did—work which
never paused and yet was never hurried—'Ohne hast, ohne
ruh.' Truly it showed that

> 'In the house of labour best
> Can I build the house of rest.'

I cannot tell how often just the thought of this house has
brought to me a sense of clearness when I have felt over-
driven and harassed."

Besides making her home a happy gathering place for
intimate friends and relatives, and a Mecca for those who
were interested in the lines of work in which she was
engaged, and who lived in other places, Mrs. Richards made
it a meeting place for the faculty and students of the Institute of Technology. She entertained the members of her own
and Professor Richards' classes every year—not at formal
receptions, but at good old-fashioned suppers, where there
was enough to eat to rejoice the heart of the boys, and
always an original entertainment afterwards. In addition to
entertaining all of their students in this way, Professor and
Mrs. Richards always invited to dinner any young man or
young woman who was specially introduced to them or who
had any special connection with them—sons and daughters of
their old schoolmates, for example, or of their old friends.
Mrs. Richards had a purpose in doing this, in addition to
that of promoting sociability. She looked with great solici-
tude upon the growing complications of life and the high
standards of living which made young people of small incomes hesitate to marry. "I like to show them what they can
have with very simple means," she said once, in writing to a
friend about the young people she invited to her house.

At the memorial meeting held by the American Home Economics Association in San Francisco during the summer of 1911, a student of the Institute of Technology, who lived in California, asked the privilege of saying something about Mrs. Richards in her personal relations. Having been given a place on the program, he made this beautiful tribute to her:

"It was in 1908 that I first reached Boston, a perfect stranger, with only a letter of introduction to Mrs. Ellen H. Richards. I took the first opportunity to present this letter, and the impression that Mrs. Richards made upon me was so striking that it will last as long as does my memory. I would like to tell those who never saw her how she appeared. Mrs. Richards was a small woman with a thin face, white hair, very black eyebrows, and eyes that sparkled with life like gems. She was active, bubbling over with energy, but most of all, she was kind.

"The previous speakers have told you how great Mrs. Richards was as an educator and as a woman, but to us, the strangers at Tech, she was greatest as a friend. Every year she had at her house an entertainment for those who came from distant parts of the world. These evenings were always informal; the men smoked and we came to know each other and Professor and Mrs. Richards. After dinner, Professor Richards would give an exhibition of glassblowing, and he always made a water hammer which later in the evening would be raffled off amidst great amusement.

"But it was not only at these little parties that the men came to know Mrs. Richards; we were always welcome at that pleasant, old-fashioned Jamaica Plain home, and I think hardly a Sunday afternoon passed but what some of the boys would call.

"In all, Mrs. Richards was a sweet and inspiring friend to us. Her hospitality was unlimited, and her kindness is a priceless memory."

This was the manner of the homemaking of the founder of the American Home Economics Association; it may well serve as a model for other women who wish to have homes and professions also.

Chapter VII

THE WOMAN'S LABORATORY

MRS. RICHARDS' marriage, by relieving her of the necessity of self-support, put her in a new economic position, and very much enlarged for her what she used to call the "region of choice." She had known what it was to be poor and to be obliged to earn her own living. Now she was to know the problems of decision which come to those who are free to choose what they will do with their time and their strength.

What she chose to do with part of her new-found time was, as we have seen, to continue her work as an analyst. In a letter written on February 15, 1876, she said that in the three preceding months she had earned two hundred and ten dollars "in her old line." But having struggled hard for her own education, and particularly for her scientific training, she wanted to bring opportunities for scientific study within easier reach of other women, and it was toward this end that a large part of her energy was directed during the next eight years. In November 1876, largely through her efforts, a Woman's Laboratory was opened at the Institute of Technology.

For the history of the movement which led up to the establishment of this laboratory we are dependent largely upon a letter that Mrs. Richards wrote in 1878. The purpose of this letter was to create interest in the laboratory and to raise money for its support; and while it was addressed to Edward Atkinson, it was evidently meant for the public. In it Mrs. Richards said that from its beginning, in 1865, the Institute of Technology had offered, in addition to its regular courses, the Lowell Free Lectures, which were open to women as well as to men. As early as 1867 these Lowell lectures had included a course in chemistry conducted by Professor Charles W. Eliot, who later became president of Harvard University, and by his associate, Professor Frank H. Storer. The following year laboratory exercises were added to the lectures, and as time went on a course in qualitative analysis was offered to those who had completed the course in general chemistry, each course, however, consisting of but fifteen lessons.

During the sixties, Mrs. Richards says in this letter, there had been a growing demand for laboratory instruction in science in the high schools and academies of New England, and this had been greatly stimulated by the publication in 1868 of Eliot and Storer's Manual of Chemistry. The result was that large numbers of women were called upon to teach chemistry and other sciences, and found themselves unprepared, particularly in laboratory methods. Almost their only opportunity to study science was in the Lowell Free Lectures.

In the fall of 1872, without previous announcement, the Lowell courses in chemistry were omitted. That fall a young woman medical student came to Boston to get instruction in qualitative analysis, only to meet with disappointment. Her case was laid before Professor James M. Crafts, of the Chemical Department of the Institute of Technology, and by him before Dr. Samuel Eliot, head master of the Girls' High School of Boston. Dr. Eliot brought the matter to the attention of the Woman's Education Association, a society of public-spirited women which had been organized less than a year before with a big purpose stated in a few words, that of "promoting the better education of women."

In an enthusiastic address before the Association, Dr. Eliot offered the use of the newly equipped chemical laboratory in his school for a class in advanced chemistry, providing the Association would raise four or five hundred dollars toward the cost of instruction and of materials for experiment. To this the Association agreed, and the class was formed in February 1873, with Miss B. T. Capen, of the Girls' High School, and Miss Swallow, of the Institute of Technology, as instructors. According to the records of the Association, the class "consisted of sixteen young women who, with perhaps two or three exceptions, were rather over than under twenty-two years of age. Fully half of them were actually engaged in teaching at the same time."

All these seem like small events when viewed from this distance, and at the time they probably passed almost unnoticed by the public; but the result of them was to bring to the attention of a strong organization the meager opportunities for scientific study offered to women, to acquaint this organization with Miss Swallow's ability as a teacher, and to win for its work her lifelong interest and support.

The following year the Lowell lectures in chemistry were resumed, but in view of the growing demand for teachers, their inadequacy became yearly more apparent. Realizing the increasing injustice of the situation, Mrs. Richards appeared before the Woman's Education Association on November 11, 1875, and in an address which made a deep impression set forth the needs of women. She expressed the belief that the governing board of the Institute of Technology would give space for a woman's laboratory if the Association would supply the necessary money for instruments, apparatus, and books. Scholarships also would be almost indispensable, she said. The Association appointed a committee to enter into communication with the Institute of Technology, with the result that the Institute offered space for a laboratory in a small frame building it was about to erect for a gymnasium, and the Woman's Education Association agreed to raise money for equipment.

How much all this meant to Mrs. Richards, and how eagerly she followed each step, we learn from her personal letters. One dated February 15, 1876, shows the project just begun. "Now I need only two thousand dollars to have a special room fitted up for ten or twelve women," she wrote. "I am making a strong effort to interest people in it, and hope to see it accomplished before I leave for Europe in June." On May 11, success was assured. The government of the Institute had only the day before passed a vote "that hereafter special students in Chemistry shall be admitted without *regard to sex.*" It had authorized a space to be fitted up for women, to be ready for use in October. Under the date of June 1, there is a happy letter reading: "We sail for Europe June 3. Miss Capen and I expect to spend lots of money in Jena for instruments. I am to purchase for the Woman's

Laboratory, which is a sure thing now. All has prospered beyond my expectations."

The new laboratory was opened in November, and was placed in charge of Professor John M. Ordway, of the Institute of Technology, with Mrs. Richards as assistant. In April 1877, Mrs. Richards reported to the Association the success of the work, saying that twenty-three students, most of whom were teachers, had been admitted. This report the president of the Association supplemented "with several important facts that Mrs. Richards' modesty rendered her reluctant to mention." These included the devotion of her whole time to the service of the students, "with no compensation whatever," the gift of two hundred and forty dollars for instruments, and last, but not least, "the payment of fifty dollars for sweeping the laboratory." We see incidentally that while the time had passed when Mrs. Richards was obliged to sweep her laboratory herself, she still found it necessary to reach down into her pocket for money with which to have it cleaned according to her standards. It should in fairness be said that the Institute of Technology was at this time passing through a financial crisis which threatened its very existence. Professor Ordway, too, gave all his available time to the laboratory without remuneration, and contributed several hundred dollars.

During the next seven years, Mrs. Richards not only worked in the Woman's Laboratory without salary, but gave an average of one thousand dollars yearly to its support.

But money was the least of all that she gave to make the laboratory a success. In those days it was necessary to help women and girls to prepare themselves to take advantage of educational opportunities, as well as to create the opportunities. We need only read letters written at the time to be reminded that what may be called the habit of ill health had taken hold of a large portion of the people, especially the women. This condition of affairs was due in part, no doubt, to helplessness in the presence of sickness; for many diseases—tuberculosis in particular—which have now come under control were then quite unchecked, and there was little known and consequently little taught about sanitation or hygiene. But whatever the cause, weakness and not health was considered the normal condition of women. It was Mrs. Richards' task, therefore, to help those who were really sick and weak, and at the same time to inspire with courage and ambition those who had fallen into the prevailing habit of thought. In doing this she showed to a very unusual degree the power to maintain the highest standard for the average women, without failing to sympathize with the sufferings of the individual woman. She advised with the students about their health, cared for them when they were sick, and took one of them, a helpless victim of tuberculosis, into her home and nursed her until her death. To another who suffered a serious nervous breakdown she gave an opportunity to go about the state and collect samples of groceries for analysis, a work which kept her much in the open air. Thus wisely did she fit special help to special needs.

Besides being handicapped by ill health, women of those days were hindered even more than now by lack of money. Parents seldom thought it so necessary that girls should be educated as that boys should be, and besides, when a girl tried to earn money for her own education she was handicapped by the smallness of her pay. Seeing the financial burden, therefore, under which many ambitious young women labored, Mrs. Richards set about securing assistance for them. We have already seen that many of the young women who studied in the laboratory during the early days were taken into her home. Several of them, too, were given oportunities to help in her professional work. In addition to this, she was constantly placing before the Woman's Education Association and before philanthropic individuals cases of special promise or urgent need. As time went on several scholarships were established and large sums of money were given to Mrs. Richards to be used in paying the expenses of the students. Among her papers have been found receipts for sums amounting to several thousand dollars which had been used for the tuition of students in the Woman's Laboratory and later for women students in the Institute of Technology itself.

But there were some students who needed neither financial help nor advice about their health, for the opportunities of the laboratory were sought by women of leisure as well as by teachers. One of these women who came into the Woman's Laboratory after having graduated from college tells a story which shows how Mrs. Richards adapted to circumstances the assistance that she gave. One day this student was carrying on a long series of weighings when she became conscious that Mrs. Richards' eye was on her. Finally Mrs. Richards came to her and said, "You are wasting motions." She had noticed that the student's hand was making two trips between the balance and the box of weights when one would have been sufficient. It was a lesson that was never forgotten, and another proof that Mrs. Richards early understood the principles of efficiency.

There were still other forms of assistance which women students of science needed in those days. It is difficult for us who live in these years of comparative freedom to realize how women who chose to walk new paths were looked upon in the days of the Woman's Laboratory. To illustrate: When, in 1876, a Boston branch of the organization later known as the Associate Alumnæ of Vassar College was formed, it was thought unwise to have the meeting for organization in a hotel, because the story that college women, who were already looked upon as a strange order of beings, had held a meeting in a public place might get into the newspapers and, by bringing added reproach, endanger the new project. As there was no private house available, it was finally decided to meet in a building which had been a private residence, but which had passed into the hands of a person who was renting it for entertainments. But even this place was semi-public, and for that reason secrecy was maintained.

In view of the attitude toward college women shown by this incident, it was necessary for those who were interested in securing the admission of girls to the Institute of Technology to proceed most cautiously, for through a little carelessness all the privileges that had been won might be forfeited. Mrs. Richards was therefore always on guard, not so much to prevent misconduct as to prevent the girls from being misunderstood and misrepresented. Her papers show that she was constantly working, oftentimes in such ways as to conceal her own connection, to keep the students from attracting unfavorable attention. The fact that such watchful care must have been extremely irksome to a person of her independent spirit indicates the magnitude of the sacrifice that she was willing to make in the cause of women's education.

In October 1877, Mrs. Richards made the following report to the Woman's Education Association: "Greater results have already accrued from the opening of the laboratory than could have been thought possible a year ago, since every department of the Institute of Technology is open to young women and any one who can pay her fees and pass the test examination can there obtain scientific education." As a result of this action on the part of the authorities of the Institute several of the special students in the Woman's Laboratory entered regular courses and graduated, and from that time on women have been on the roll of students. But from all parts of the country women, particularly teachers, were coming to get special help. Partly for this reason, and partly because the other laboratories were crowded, the Woman's Laboratory was maintained until the year 1883, when a new building which had been erected by the Institute gave space for all the students, women as well as men.

From the circumstances under which the Woman's Laboratory was started, it was natural that the students whom it drew should need much individual attention. There was little uniformity either in the character of the preparation that they had received or in the amount of time they were able to devote to the work. In the letter of 1878 to which reference was made early in this chapter, Mrs. Richards stated that she believed that such conditions must exist for many years. She wrote: "The methods of instruction are at present adapted to the individual and to the length of time at her disposal. For the next ten years the teaching must be largely of this special and unusual character if it is to do the most good. Women of twenty-five years of age have missed the scientific education of the present day, yet they ask for and must have the knowledge of the present. The laboratory was opened to meet this very want, and while it will strive to create new and wider fields for women's work in the professional branches of applied chemistry, it will hold as its first duty the teaching of those who cannot go back into the schools and colleges."

The following letters show how valuable the laboratory was to the teachers of that time.

Cora Pike, formerly of Wheaton Seminary, writes: "During the sixties, the study of chemistry at Wheaton Seminary was mostly confined to the textbook, supplemented once a year by a course of lectures from an itinerant expert, who with his tanks of various gases produced highly spectacular effects.

"It was during the seventies that news of Mrs. Richards' laboratory for women reached the Seminary. The teacher of chemistry at once appealed to Mrs. Richards for advice. She cordially invited her to come to Boston on Saturdays, offering all assistance possible. Mrs. Richards must have felt it an additional tax upon herself, for the laboratory was filled to overflowing with regular students; but there were no intimations of the kind, and a course of independent work was planned with special reference to the classes at Wheaton.

"So much, indeed, was interest in experimental science awakened by work with Mrs. Richards in Boston and at the Seminary, that in 1878 it was decided to build a chemical laboratory for the school. Plans for it were suggested by Mrs. Richards, and her enthusiastic interest in all the natural sciences led to the construction of a room where classes in chemistry, mineralogy, botany, physics, and biology could be equally well accommodated. After a few years, the old order at Wheaton Seminary was changed by Mrs. Richards' guiding hand, and natural science was studied in the light of individual experiment."

Anna George, who at the time of Mrs. Richards' death was eighty-six years old and had been blind for many years, wrote: "It was during the seventies, while I was a teacher in the Brighton High School, that it was my great privilege to study chemistry with Mrs. Richards. How memory leaps over the years as I try to recall her as she then was, so *alert* and *enthusiastic* and so *kind* and *friendly!* To her 'life was real, life was earnest,' and how she strove to impress upon us the importance of turning to good account all the knowledge we gained! My experience in teaching chemistry was a very happy and successful one, and I am sure this was largely owing to the inspiration as well as to the excellent qualities of the instruction received from my teacher."

Mary Evans, for many years president of Lake Erie College at Painesville, Ohio, says: "The connection of Mrs. Richards with Lake Erie College began during the early years of the Woman's Laboratory. I was deeply interested in new opportunities in science for women, and the interest was taking a practical form, for we were building, in 1876, our first addition and were planning space in it for a chemical laboratory and a museum. We were enlarging all our courses, and in 1878 our teacher of chemistry and botany was given leave of absence to study at the Institute of Technology. Through letters from her we had our first glimpse of Mrs. Richards as a woman of broad vision and executive ability, and of the home at Jamaica Plain, with its cordial welcome to students, its flowers and pets and atmosphere of ordered peace, a type and prophecy of homes to be influenced hereafter by the voice and pen of Mrs. Richards. Later others of our teachers studied at the Institute of Technology, and our admiration for Mrs. Richards deepened and her name became a household word in later years."

Among the other institutions to which teachers went out from the Woman's Laboratory were Wellesley College, Smith College, Pennsylvania College, the Framingham Normal School, Bradford Seminary, Quincy Mansion School, the Mary A. Burnham Classical School, and high schools in Boston and elsewhere.

The Woman's Laboratory having been established and put upon a firm basis so far as standards of instruction were concerned, the attention of the students was directed towards women's special problems. It was Mrs. Richards' hope that many of them would devote themselves to the analysis of foods and of cleaning materials. She herself was doing some work in this line at the time, the result of which was the publication of two small books. "The Chemistry of Cooking and Cleaning," and "Food Materials and Their Adulterations." In preparing these books, Mrs. Richards was so farsighted that although they were published in 1881 and 1885, there was after thirty years an increasing demand for them in revised editions.

It would be unwise, of course, to hazard an opinion as to what might have happened if this work in household chemistry had been taken up by a large number of women and pursued with that enthusiasm which Mrs. Richards felt for it at the time. It is safe to say, however, that if the work had extended as she hoped it would, upward as well as downward in the schools, the practice of sophisticating foods which owed its baneful success largely to women's ignorance would never have reached large and wasteful proportions.

With the action of the Institute of Technology taken in 1878, by which girls were admitted to the Institute on exactly the same footing as boys, Mrs. Richards was not in full sympathy. She believed that it would be wiser not to admit them until the third year. She was overruled, and wisely perhaps, but her objections, though based on an enthusiastic overestimate of the demand for scientific education, were very characteristic of her attitude of mind.

Her first objection had its root in her fixed belief that it was unwise for women to demand special privileges. "Military drill is required for the first and second years. No one would wish the women to drill, and the presence of any favored class in any institution is unprofitable."

Her second objection was based on an appreciation of the dangers of intermittent coeducation. Then, girls and boys were separated in the grammar schools and high schools of Boston. *"I believe most heartily in coeducation from the earliest childhood,* but have seen enough to convince me that it must be continuous and not have an interregnum of the years from seven to fifteen and then begin." It is significant that more than thirty years after she made this statement, the same arguments were brought up in Boston with reference to bringing the boys and girls together in the high schools after they had been separated in the lower grades.

"Finally," she said, "and to my mind the most fundamental of all, though it grieves me to say it, the present state of public opinion among women themselves does not give reason to believe that, of one hundred young girls of sixteen who might enter if the opportunity was offered, ten would carry the course through. It is demoralizing to have such results in the early stage of scientific education for women." Exactly what Mrs. Richards meant by "the present state of public opinion" cannot be known, but it is probable that she had in mind not only the accepted belief that women had little physical endurance, but also the fact that unreasonable demands upon their time and foolish social conventions were allowed to interfere with their opportunity to make systematic preparation for professional work.

In 1882, when a new building for the chemical laboratory was finally assured, Mrs. Richards wrote the following letter, most of which was afterwards embodied in a circular: "The question of space in the new building for the suitable accommodation of women students has been weighing upon my mind for the last two or three weeks, and after consultation with General Walker, Miss Crocker, Miss Abby May, and Miss Florence Cushing, we have made ourselves a self-constituted committee to obtain subscriptions from women interested in the education of women toward a small sum, say eight or ten thousand dollars, which may be put into the hands of the corporation, in order that they may feel justified in including in the plans suitable toilet rooms in connection with each of the laboratories and a reception room somewhere in the building which shall be for their use only. If this can be done, the Institute can then say that it is in a condition to receive women."

Before the necessary sum of money was raised, one of the first and most promising students of the Woman's Laboratory, Margaret Cheney, the only child of Mrs. Ednah D. Cheney, a great-souled woman of Boston, interested in every phase of the battle for human freedom, died suddenly. In her honor the rest room in the building was named The Margaret Cheney Room. Money was contributed by many people, but the work of planning the room, of selecting its pictures and furnishings, and of carrying on the voluminous correspondence which always attends co-operative undertakings, fell to Mrs. Richards. The Margaret Cheney Room has ever since been the center of the life of the women students of the Institute of Technology.

In 1883, the Woman's Laboratory building was torn down, and the special service which Mrs. Richards did in superintending its work came to an end. On July of that year, weary from her overwhelming labors, she wrote this pathetic letter: "I feel like a woman whose children are all about to be married and leave her alone, so that she is to move into a smaller house and a new neighborhood. You see it is quite a change for me, and though I knew it was coming, I cannot at once fit all the corners. My work is done and happily done, but the energy will have to be used somehow and that is the question. The case is this: We women have raised ten thousand dollars and given to the Institute to make suitable provision for women students in all departments. The new building, equal in size nearly to the old, is to be ready in October. In that are to be the chemical laboratories, the ladies' parlor and reading room, etc. Our present women's laboratory will be torn down and my duties will be gone, as I shall not go into the new laboratory. Now I would not mind if I was away at the Lake out of it all or if I knew where to store my apparatus, but everything is so unsettled, owing to the uncertainty, as I do not know that I shall have anything to do or anywhere to work. Professor Richards is to have a new mining laboratory and Professor Ordway a new industrial chemical laboratory and I shall have some sort of work between them, but that will not be this year.

"Then changes always disturb me. Professor Richards' work this summer is on an electrical process and I cannot help him much, and he can't give me time to go to drive or to look over the library papers and drawers and my day does not seem to amount to anything. . . . I should be perfectly happy anywhere if I could have him with me, for we always harmonize; but to have him charged with electricity so that he cannot think of anything else and to have no definite plans and heaps of things to do and no life to do them is a little hard. . . Everything seems to fall flat and I have a sense of impending fate which is paralyzing."

Soon afterwards Mrs. Richards was given a place on the faculty of the Institute of Technology, and from that time on she performed, in addition to her instructional work, all the duties of Dean of Women, although she was never given that title. Nor did she ever wish it. She has left on record her belief that "a Dean of Women is out of place in a coeducational institution." She continued, however, to watch over women students in sickness and in health, in their work and in their pleasures. She sought financial aid for them and opportunities for them to earn money; chaperoned their parties, often remaining far into the evening after a long day's work, and, more often than they suspected, paying all the expenses of the entertainment; raised money for a woman's gymnasium and superintended its construction; watched the papers for unfavorable criticism of the students and sought every means of bringing their work to the attention of the people in helpful ways; secured positions for them and advised them after they entered upon their professional work. She was, in short, as one of them has said, "their elder sister and their foster mother."

Chapter VIII

TEACHING BY CORRESPONDENCE

WHAT Mrs. Richards did for the education of those who were able to go to college or who needed only a little encouragement or a little financial assistance to enable them to do so is but a fraction of what she did for women's education. She herself, as we know, had remained at home in a small country town until she was twenty-five years of age, longing for a broader view, hungering and thirsting after knowledge. It was not surprising, therefore, considering her early experiences and her missionary spirit, that when shortly after her marriage she was asked to take part in the work of a society for the encouragement of studies at home she gladly accepted the opportunity. It may be, too, that the newness of the venture and its novelty, at a time when teaching by correspondence was almost unknown, appealed to her adventurous spirit, and offered her an alluring chance to pioneer.

The Society to Encourage Studies at Home, which came to be known among busy people as Studies at Home, or merely by its initials, S.H., was founded in 1873 chiefly through the instrumentality of Anna Eliot Ticknor, daughter of the historian, a woman to whom much had been given in the way of educational advantages and contact with intellectual people, and who recognized her own obligations to give much to others in return. The headquarters of the society were for many years in the Ticknor home, a historic building at 9 Park Street, in one of the most conspicuous situations on Beacon Hill.

Papers from an English organization called The Society for Encouragement of Home Study fell into Miss Ticknor's hands at a time when the intellectual needs of isolated women and those who were necessarily kept much at home were uppermost in her mind. She was quick to act, and the result was the organization of the American society which for twenty-five years proved a source of help and encouragement to thousands of women. Miss Ticknor acted as secretary until the time of her death, in 1896, when the society was discontinued.

The American society differed from the English in not confining its benefits to rich women of leisure. In fact, it sought chiefly to help busy women by showing them how to make profitable use of the small amount of time at their disposal for systematic reading. Nor did it make the mistake of supposing that isolated women are to be found only in rural districts. "The craving mind," said Mrs. Richards in one of her annual reports, "may be as isolated in a city full of all the advantages which it desires as if it were far from books, museums, and kindred minds."

The organizers of the society, ten in number, were themselves women of broad education, and they had the benefit of advice and assistance from many prominent educators. When Mrs. Richards associated herself with it, therefore, she found it doing thorough, systematic, scholarly work. This was, however, chiefly in the subjects that can most easily be taught by correspondence—history, language, and literature. It was for her to devise a plan for teaching those subjects that demand laboratory methods. The organization of its work in science was her most important contribution to the society. In this, as in every other line of education, she exhibited a remarkable combination of high ideals and standards for the work itself and of sympathy with the trials, shortcomings, and failures of individual students.

The beginnings of the Science Section are thus described in a memorial volume published after Miss Ticknor's death: "In view of the fact that in 1873 science was only partially recognized as an element in a liberal education, and the laboratory method was yet in its infancy, it seems an almost prophetic insight which included science in the list of topics upon which courses were offered. It is undoubtedly due to the influence of that great teacher, Louis Agassiz, that this forward step was taken, and it was by his advice, and with his persuasion, that the charge of the course was taken for the first two years by the woman who was at that time a most ardent advocate of the study of science as an elevating and enriching factor in education. Miss Lucretia Crocker had imbibed deeply of the spirit of Agassiz's teaching, and from the first adopted his watchword, 'Study from specimens, not from books.' "

The Science Department came into Mrs. Richards' hands in January 1876, after Miss Crocker had been appointed Supervisor of Schools in Boston, and in September of the same year, upon the reorganization of the work, she became head of what was known as the Science Section. She taught geology, mineralogy, and physical geography, and had general supervision of the teaching of botany, geology, and mathematics.

Books, microscopes and other apparatus, laboratory material—minerals and herbariums—were sent by mail. With these in the students' hands the correspondence opened. "We aim to unclasp for our students the book of nature," Mrs. Richards said in one of her annual reports, "and bid them look within. We hope to inspire a love for the truths of nature, as well as stimulate a search for facts. In method, the study of science might be defined as the art of asking questions—not as the spoiled child asks, for the sake of getting answers; and, while students are taught to question the things themselves, the teacher always leaves an open door for questions on ways of investigating and on the meanings of observations."

Into the teaching of science and "the unclasping of the book of nature" for others, Mrs. Richards seems to have entered with all the enthusiasm with which she had entered upon her own studies. The great majority of the students in the society were, of course, in the sections devoted to the humanities, but the science students, though few in number, caught their leader's spirit. "I took up this new study (mineralogy)," wrote one of them in 1883, "because I wanted to know something about it and also that I might be one of the enthusiasts in the 'science corner' at the annual meetings of the society. The enthusiasm of the few in your department was so inspiring that I have wanted for two years to join the band, and now find leisure to do so."

"I received the portfolio on Saturday," wrote another. ". . . It has supplied a want I had to see a herbarium started." And another, "This year every bud was interesting, and I shall hope to continue next year." And still another: "What a revelation! The horse-chestnut had never been a favorite of mine, and now every little twig has a meaning."

A student who has since made a name for herself and contributed much to the solution of problems of public health wrote: "The explanations you sent me were very clear and just what I wanted, and I am very much obliged for them. Indeed I cannot tell you how very grateful I feel for this help you give me. To take so much interest in a complete stranger and to give up so much time and trouble to me! I only hope I shall some day know enough to be able to help some girl as you are helping me, for that is the only way I could ever pay off my obligation to you."

One woman who, because of the unconventional mode of life adopted by her family, was completely ostracized during the years of her young womanhood writes: "For a number of years I corresponded with her. How could she ever have spared the time! Bless her! Her correspondence and interest were my mainstay through the most difficult years of my girlhood and lasted into middle life."

Another student, a clerk and bookkeeper in a general backwoods store, who wrote when she joined the society, "It is no use to go on geological trips, for there are not any rocks about here (you must remember that I live in the woods)," sent on a little later twenty specimens, among which were several varieties of fossil corals. In her subsequent letters she often spoke of "something new" which she had found while walking or riding. Still another student found fossils in a marble mantelpiece. Another wrote, "I have eyes to see now what I have never seen before."

There was apparently no limit to the help which poured from Mrs. Richards' study in Boston to struggling, perplexed women. She drew diagrams of convenient house plans and of sanitary arrangements for drainage and plumbing. She helped them to plan their dress. "If it is a relief to take your clothes off at night," she wrote to one after giving specific directions for healthful dressing, "be sure that something is wrong. I know of no better rule to go by. Clothes should not be a burden. They should be a comfort and a protection." And to others:

"As to dress, I find ———— a very helpful publication. It is much more suitable than most such papers, and the letters from Paris give one an idea of the general principle of dress often a year before they are seen on the street; and while there are few costumes that I should want to wear, yet hints can be gleaned which with a little adaptation serve to keep one from going so far from the usual way as to be remarked. I believe in using materials one likes and in keeping one's self comfortable, but it is very wise to go unremarked in a crowd."

"You are quite right to give up a *parlor*. I think it is the mistake of our country people to shut up one room for company. You can easily manage your dining room to serve as a sitting room, and if people come at meal time, well, let them. What matter such trifles after all. They won't mind *if you don't*. There is the point—do what you think wise and stick to it; never mind. If you keep your feathers well oiled the water of criticism will run off as from a duck's back. Write again, please."

In addition to help in these specific problems, she sent cheer and encouragement. To one who had passed through harrowing trials she wrote: "Your notes are very good indeed, and even though you may feel that they do not represent much work done, yet a little is something, and often an occupation of the mind helps the body. I know that we cannot always overcome physical weakness; indeed, I have had experience this winter; but we can avoid many troubles by a proper mental condition. I do not wonder you are not strong now, and you must remember that when the mind has been strained it loses its control of the body, and the way to come back is to bring the body into as good a condition as possible. A little change is the best thing, but with Baby to care for, that is not easy to get. Still, if possible, get it after a fashion. Now that spring is here, get out of doors."

To another whose work had been interrupted by weeks of illness, and who sent a regretful explanation instead of her usual monthly report, she wrote: "The Society for Home Study is to encourage, not to urge. You must not get discouraged. I often think that all the difficulties we encounter only give us the more strength if we keep hold of our work, and we must not now give up while in the prime of life. It is best to keep trying, and by and by the opportunity will come. If we have given up, then we shall not be ready for it when it does come."

To others she sent such cheering messages as these:

"I do not see why you should give up. What if you get only three afternoons in the month to work; is that not something? If I have an expectation of hearing from you once a month, will not that be a help? It is only two months more, and it seems a pity to quite give up. You know our society is for just such people, to give what aid and sympathy is required."

"We never can tell how our lives may work to the account of the general good, and we are not wise enough to know if we have fulfilled our mission or not. How do you know that your unsatisfied longings may not be so transmuted in your little daughter as to make her a pioneer or a leader in some great work for the good of mankind? If you had had all you wanted, you could not have given her the wish, the strength perhaps, to be what she may be now. Most heroes and heroines have sprung from such homes as yours. I have just been reading Besant's 'Inner House,' and I have been especially struck with the thought there brought out that all progress and even all enjoyment is dependent upon the frailty of human life and human desires—that if we were to have all we want and to live forever, all enjoyment would be gone."

It must be remembered that this work was carried on without a stenographer. The mere physical effort must have been a severe drain upon her strength, but there is no suggestion that explanation or advice was ever curtailed to save herself.

In looking over Mrs. Richards' papers I continually found references to people living in regions remote from Boston, in Canada and the far West, some of them in isolated mountain regions or on ranches, and I wondered what had brought them to her acquaintance. Many of them proved to be friends whom she had made on the trips taken with Professor

Richards in connection with his engineering work, but a surprisingly large number proved to be students in Studies at Home. In a majority of the cases, the friendships thus started were kept up, and Mrs. Richards did much to cement them by seeking out her former pupils as she traveled from place to place.

Margaret Sheppard, of Philadelphia, who came to be an intimate friend, writes: "For nearly eight years it was my privilege to be an instructor in the Society for Home Study, with Mrs. Richards as my chief. Warmly interested, from its start, in the success of the society, it was wonderful how, amid her many claims, she *made* time to put so much of herself into its work. The teachers under her found an ever-ready helper, and the student's problems she made her own. The Boston girl who discovered crinoid stems in the marble mantel delighted her; and she was equally interested in the woman on a farm who propped her book open to study while scrubbing the floor.

"At that time I had pupils also in a Philadelphia Society for Home Culture which admitted young men to its ranks. One of these, a Western farmer with unique experiences, strongly attracted Mrs. Richards, and frequently when we met she would ask, 'How is A No. 1?' Once when I was at a loss how to give this youth the instruction in blowpipe work which he desired, she generously wrote nearly six pages of diagrams and explanations, showing where the flame was hottest and how the blowpipe could be used to best advantage."

But the joy that was brought into homes by means of the teaching of science or of nature study, if you will, was not confined to the older people. In 1881 a student wrote: "I find the little I have learned a great delight to the children, twelve, six, and three years of age. The six-year-old boy pores over the specimens with the glass, and often insists upon my leaving my work to 'come and see this remarkable thing God has made.' "

In many cases the students were "shut-ins." One of these, writing to Mrs. Richards, said: "I am grateful for your kind, interesting letter received a few days ago. I will try to give you some idea of my life as you wish. . . . I have been an invalid, confined to the house a greater part of the time, for nine years. I do not go out at all through the winter, but am able to go around the yard and fields some of the time through the summer."

As time went on, the same difficulty arose in connection with the Society to Encourage Studies at Home that had arisen in connection with the higher education of women. Few were able to do continuous work, and excuses on the ground of ill health came with almost every letter. This troubled every one interested in the welfare of the society, and the result was the publication of a carefully prepared tract on Health, which, though it does not bear Mrs. Richards' name, was written by her. Those who were connected with the earlier work of the society say that this tract, as it left her hands, was much more extended and much more plainspoken than it was when it finally appeared. While it may not, therefore, have been in its completed form all that she would have had it, it carried helpful suggestions and valuable advice to thousands of homes. It was sent to every student who was enrolled, and had a somewhat extended sale outside of the society. It treated not only of the external conditions for right living, of fresh air, sunlight, good food, and healthful dress, but also, and in a way which was much in advance of the times, of certain mental conditions affecting health, as the following extracts show:

"By nature the nervous organization of women, particularly of American women, is more sensitive than that of men, and many things in the present system of education and of living tend to make it still more so.

"Contrast the lives of schoolgirls and schoolboys out of school hours. A boy, not only by his own instinct, but by command of those who wish to get rid of his restless presence in the house, is out of doors every free moment, and usually in active motion. A girl, after school is over, is apt to be told, 'You must have some exercise, I suppose, so go now and take a walk, but do not be gone long; and remember you have an hour's practicing to do, and then you must work on the trimming for your dress, or it will not be finished in time.' The girl naturally returns to her lessons with nerves a little more weary than when she left them.

"After school days are over, the girls, whom the present system of education, culminating in public exhibition and competition, has left to suffer from reaction, find no natural connection between their school life and the new one on which they enter, and are apt to be aimless, if not listless, needing external stimulus, and finding it only prepared for them, it may be, in some form of social excitement.

"Schoolgirls, then, need out-of-door life; girls after leaving school need intellectual interests, well regulated and not encroaching on home duties. 'We must suppress the inordinate desire for acquiring knowledge from books and schools in infancy and childhood, and stimulate those who have passed their youth to apply themselves with great vigor to mental improvement.'

"There are women in middle life, whose days are crowded with practical duties, physical strain, and moral responsibility, who need this last injunction; for they fail to see that some use of the mind, in solid reading or in study, would refresh them by its contrast with carking cares, and would prepare interest and pleasure for their later years. Such women often sink into depression, as their cares fall away from them, and many even become insane. They are mentally starved to death.

.   .   .   .

"There is still an extremely important division of the subject to be touched upon," she said toward the close. "This is the *study and acceptance of personal limitations.* For want of this grasp of one's individual situation, many a life is wasted. By a quiet and sensible appreciation of it, many feeble lives and narrow abilities have been made useful, some even distinguished. . . . A mistaken view of duty is also to be guarded against. It is cowardly to fly from natural duties and take up those that suit our taste or temperament better; but it is also unwise to take an exaggerated view of personal duties, which shuts out the proper care of the mind and body entrusted to us.

"Lest these remarks sound vague, let us illustrate them: A woman, busy with the cares of her family, fails to study and to place at their true value her duties to her mind as well as to her body and to her household. She makes no mental progress as the years go on, loses the power of companionship with her children, grows discontented and fretful, and passes the last years of her life in dull, ignorant unhappiness. Had she seen the limitations and laws of her physical and mental nature, she would have known that it was not selfish to snatch a half-hour every day for the refreshment of her mind in a botanizing walk, or a quiet time for thinking in the open air, or to lock her chamber door while she read two or three pages of a good author. . . .

"In short, if we would be and do all that as a rational being we should desire, we must resolve to govern ourselves; we must seek diversity of interests; dread to be without an object and without mental occupation; and try to balance work for the body and work for the mind."

In 1886 a new section, Sanitary Science, was established in the society. The plan of this course was an original idea with Mrs. Richards. It was at a time when household conveniences employing water, gas, or electricity were becoming general, but housekeepers seldom understood what dangers and difficulties attended the ignorant use of the new arrangements. She saw that instruction was needed, and was glad to make the society a means to that end and to spread abroad knowledge of the possibilities of organizing the house on truly scientific principles. The subject at once aroused great enthusiasm. A student wrote that she found it so full of interest that she dropped all other studies in order to devote herself to Sanitary Science in its most practical applications. Another, already at work along these lines in her home city, found books recommended by her correspondent of greatest help in her study groups organized in every ward of her city. Many other students became centers from which started widening circles of intelligent interest in right living.

If we were to try to sum up Mrs. Richards' contributions to the society, we should find included not only her work of planning and teaching, and her unmeasured and immeasurable acts of kindness to individual students, but also wise advice given as a member of the Executive Committee in the councils of the society. Here she always insisted on high standards of work. "It seems to me," she said to a fellow-instructor, "that influence which is exerted in so many centers ought to be the best possible. We ought to be scientific in our methods, and we ought to require scientific execution on the part of students. I am now ready to make more strict plans. My students have shown themselves capable of good work, work of which I am not ashamed. Shall we not endeavor to bring our standards a little higher?"

It was through her advice that the work of the society was so modified and extended as to make it meet the needs of college graduates. In 1883, when the recently organized Association of Collegiate Alumnæ was endeavouring to promote graduate study among its members, there were few opportunities for such study in the colleges themselves, and Mrs. Richards laid before the association a plan for inducing alumnæ to join the Society for Encouraging Studies at Home; to the society itself she proposed certain changes in the routine of its work which would adapt it better to this purpose. As a result, a Correspondence University was started in connection with the society. This soon passed beyond its usefulness because of enlarging opportunities offered by universities, but for a time it met a great need.

At every step in the work, whether it involved a change in methods of teaching or the adoption of a new textbook, Mrs. Richards consulted the very best authorities on the subject in the country. In her own work on minerals she was in constant correspondence with Richard H. Dana, the geologist. No opportunity to gain information was ever lost. The woman who wrote to her from Germany to know of the work of the society received abundant assistance, but she must have soon become aware that she had entered into correspondence with a woman as eager for information as herself, for Mrs. Richards plied her with questions concerning the conditions of correspondence work in her own country.

In 1893, when Mrs. Richards had charge of the Rumford Kitchen at the World's Fair in Chicago, she accepted the added work and responsibility of arranging an exhibition of the work of Studies at Home. "Your letter came this morning," wrote Miss Ticknor on September 5, 1893, "and I look with awe at all your preparations and the work before you at Chicago. It is fine that you can accomplish so much and so serenely. The work of S. H. goes on well, but we do not feel quite made up and shall not until you come back."

But work and workers always react, one upon the other, and as I have studied Mrs. Richards' connection with this correspondence work, it has been with a growing sense of its important bearing upon her own later activities. For many years after she left home to attend college, her life was spent chiefly in academic institutions and among highly educated people. To a certain extent it had tended to shut out the problems of the everyday life with which the great masses of the people were struggling. Her teaching by correspondence doubtless served to bring before her in very vivid manner the needs of the average home. May it not be that in Studies at Home lay the foundation of her great work of later years?

Chapter IX

BEGINNINGS OF EUTHENICS

CONVICTION that the world was full of unnecessary sickness, and that men and women were falling far short of the joy of living and of doing which ought to be theirs, grew upon Mrs. Richards with her experiences in the Woman's Laboratory and with her insight through correspondence into the home life of America. With the conviction came the desire to have a part in removing this deplorable handicap. *"We must see to that,"* she once wrote in her diary, after recording a grievous social injustice which had been brought to her attention. *"See to it"* she did in the matter of preventable disease, for from the moment of her own conviction she labored unceasingly wherever and with whomsoever she saw an opportunity to improve the material conditions of living. She came in the course of time to be prominently identified with the home economics movement. But this was only part of the great, absorbing interest of her life, which included the bettering of conditions in the community, in the school, and in the factory, as well as in the home. This larger and more inclusive interest, though neither named nor defined by her until shortly before her death, early took full possession of her powers, and the last thirty years of her life were given to developing the "science of controllable environment," for which she coined the name "Euthenics."

Her preparation for leadership in this work had been begun in the careful training that she received from her mother in the household arts. This physical education she considered an essential element in the control of external things, and repeatedly during her later life she attributed the failure of individuals to reach their highest efficiency to the fact that they had not received in early life the necessary muscle training. In speaking of college women who, when they become housekeepers, expect that tasks involving manual dexterity will come easy to them because of what they consider their comprehensive preparation for life, she said:

"The head can save the heels only when the heels have had practice young and remember *without telling* what to do at the slightest hint. In other words, *housework* is a trade to be prepared for by manual exercise, as *housekeeping* is a profession to be prepared for by mental exercise." She said in connection with an abortive attempt to train educated and intelligent but inexperienced women as "Household Aids," and thus to dignify domestic service, "Intelligence did not make up for lack of early muscle training."

As a result of the great importance which she attached to the early education of the hand, she became one of the first advocates of manual training in the public schools, and throughout her life she was interested, not only in the introduction of such work, but in the improvement of its methods and in its adjustment to other departments of school work. As early as 1881, when the Associated Charities of Boston was urging the introduction of manual training into the schools, its secretary submitted to her a list of questions. These and her unequivocal and farseeing answers follow:

Question. When should industrial education begin? *Answer.* As early as anything is taught. Children are always eager to *do something.* The girl of four or five years tries to cut out her doll's clothes or to do anything that she sees done. The boy of the same age is always eager for a jack-knife and a hammer. It would seem as if Nature pointed the way in this instinct to use the hands first. It is cruelty to children to keep five-year-olds sitting still, gazing into vacancy even for one hour at a time. We have little idea of the torture we thus inflict.

Question. With what methods, the "Russian" or a more direct plan? *Answer.* The principle of the Russian method, to use whatever will train the hand and eye without regard to the product, seems to be the only one adapted to children from five to ten years of age. No finished product can be expected from the little hands, and they should be allowed free scope, not scolded and punished because they spoil the material. Do not older people learn most by their mistakes? Hence the *end* of first instruction should be the child's own improvement regardless of the material used. After these four or five years of training, particular branches may well be taught.   Experience only can answer just when this teaching can best begin, for in the first step in manual training the work must be subordinate to the child.

Question.   Might not some of the more purely scholastic studies be profitably eliminated in favor of eye and hand training? *Answer.*   At first they may need to be at least postponed, but it is my firm conviction that the industrial training from five to ten years of age will so quicken the powers of body and mind that the studies now deemed irksome will be carried on with great ease and pleasure in conjunction with manual exercises.

Question.   Would a supplementary course be desirable, or should it be a part of the regular course? *Answer.*   I believe that it should form an essential part of the regular course.   This is the view from a purely educational standpoint, without considering the trouble of moving the present elaborate structure of our schools.   A supplementary course may be the wiser plan to begin; it would be wiser than none.

This earnest plea for the training which enables the body to do the bidding of the mind, and which tends to bring it under subjection to the will, was in line with her steadfast belief that education should make man master of his environment.   But she urged also, and from the very first of her interest in schools, that scientific education which teaches how natural forces may be directed toward chosen ends was also essential to the control of material things.   This conviction had its beginning, no doubt, in the instruction which she received at Vassar under Professor Farrar.   Hardly a week of her college life passed when she did not record some interesting connection between the facts and discoveries of science and the phenomena and problems of common life.

One letter showed that she had discovered why fresh bread was indigestible, and another why it is possible to beat the whites of eggs into a foam.   The lectures on air, too, found an appreciative listener.   "Professor Farrar has been telling us some interesting and startling facts with reference to air and the subject of ventilation. . . . He had a bedroom with glass sides about three feet high and wide, in which he put six people to bed (six wax tapers at different heights), one in a trundle bed near the floor, another a little higher, and so on, up to a high bed near the ceiling. He shut all the windows to keep out the *night air*. They lived from one-half to one minute. Then he opened the windows at the top, as people generally do, and they lived only a minute at the bottom, though the highest ones lived some time longer. Again he shut the top windows and opened the bottom; about the same result, only the lower one lived longest. With a current of air from top to bottom, all lived indefinitely.

"Consumption is the result of the *tight building* of the present day. We should all die if people could succeed as they wish. A fireplace is better than life insurance. . . . Dr. Bell, of Boston, found that every one of the people in Massachusetts who was over one hundred years old was brought up in an open fireplace. (When the girls laughed, Professor Farrar said he could say so, for the favorite corner of the children used to be in the *chimney corner,* where they could study astronomy.)"

But even more important than this awakened interest in the relation of science to practical affairs was a realization of the possibility of controlling external conditions in a large way and for the benefit of all the people. This came a little later through the analytical work which she did upon air and food for the State Board of Health. The chain was now nearly complete; she was almost ready to set forth as teacher and preacher. Toward this end the constant challenge which came to her from friends and associates to prove the value of the knowledge which she was accumulating may have contributed. About two years after she entered the Institute of Technology, her old friend and teacher at Westford Academy, Addison Smith, wrote: "I suppose you are at work in the dirt yet" (referring doubtless to her mineralogical work). "You will turn out a professor of dust and ashes, I presume, and be glad some time to accept an offer to keep some old widower's premises clean with the aid of a broom, dustpan, mop, etc. Then you can analyze the contents of the dustpan and be able to solve some problem in the chemistry of cuisine." The following year he wrote: "Haven't you nearly learned out? Can you analyze a loaf of bread yet? I bet you can't make a good loaf,"

Of course the joke was the other way, for she was an efficient housekeeper as well as a chemist, and the effect of these pleasantries was to make her search more deeply for the connection between facts of science and needs of life.

The time had, in fact, come when neither more knowledge nor a clearer understanding of conditions was necessary to her preparation for leadership, but a motive strong enough to compel her to formulate her own ideas and plans. This came in the winter of 1879, when Maria Mitchell invited her to give an address before the women of Poughkeepsie on "Chemistry in Relation to Household Economy." The address was delivered before three hundred women in March 1879 so successfully that Maria Mitchell used to say, "I discovered Mrs. Richards." Following is the substance of this lecture:

"It may interest some of your number, those who like to follow out the evolution of thought, to know how and why this idea of the application of science in general, and chemistry in particular, came to take so strong a hold upon my mind. You will see that, as is often the case, it was partly due to contrariness. We often overlook the bearing of our work until some one who does not believe in it shows us how much we might do. One day some one said to me, 'What good do you expect this will do in the kitchen?' I have never succeeded in banishing the ring of that question from my ears. . . . It has been repeated in other forms so many times since that I have had little opportunity to forget.

"A few weeks since, the door of the laboratory opened to admit two women a little past middle life, though not old. They came in with wondering looks, as they saw several young women at work in the room. . . . I attempted to satisfy their curiosity by speaking of those who studied chemistry for the purpose of knowing something of its principles and applications. They did not seem to understand this motive, and I proceeded to tell them of the teachers who were now required to teach science and who must learn laboratory work in order to secure better salaries. This fact appealed to them somewhat, but one immediately asked, 'What good is it going to do for domestic women?' To this question, which doubtless comes first to many when the subject of scientific teaching for girls is discussed, 'What good will it do for domestic women?' I shall try to suggest an answer, at least in part.

"Now it is often stated that our educational system unfits the girls for their work in life, which is largely that of house-keepers. It cannot be the knowledge which unfits them. One can never know too much of things which one is to handle. Can a railroad engineer know too much about the parts of his engine? Can the cotton manufacturer know too much about cotton fiber? Can a cook know too much about the composition and nutritive value of the meats and vegetables which she uses? Can a housekeeper know too much of the effect of fresh air on the human system, of the danger of sewer gas, of foul water?

"It cannot be the knowledge of *things* which unfits the youth to handle the things themselves. It must be that some sort of false logic has crept into our schools, for the people whom I have seen doing housework or cooking know nothing of botany or chemistry, and the people who know botany and chemistry do not cook or sweep. The conclusion seems to be, if one knows chemistry she must not cook or do house-work.

"If we look narrowly at the teaching of botany and chemistry and the other so-called natural sciences in most of our public schools, we may wonder less that this reason-ing has gained a foothold. (Then follows an arraignment of the schools for not teaching application of sciences.)

"Scientific facts are taught, to be sure, but in just the same way and often by the same teachers as historical facts are taught. Girls, and boys too, may learn that there is such a thing as a soluble oxalate of iron, without learning that because ink contains iron, oxalic acid will therefore form a soluble compound with ink stains. The trouble lies in the lack of actual knowledge of *things,* and the attempt to supply this lack by certain theoretical ideas which have no more relation to every-day life than the wars of the Crusaders. . . .

"Girls may learn that rice is a carbohydrate, and that peas and beans are not only carbohydrates but also albuminoids, without learning the connection of these facts with every-day life. The best authorities who have studied the nutritive value of various foods state that a strong working man requires, per day, 420 grams of carbohydrates to keep up the animal heat and 120 grams of albuminoids to repair the waste of tissue. Two pounds of peas or beans will much more than furnish these constituents at a cost of about ten cents at ordinary prices. Six or seven eggs and one pound of rice will come near furnishing both, but at an average cost of fourteen cents to twenty-one cents. Three-quarters of a pound of cheese will give the albuminoids at a cost of, say eighteen cents. Four pounds of potatoes will give the starch, but twenty-five pounds of potatoes will be required for the albuminoids. Hence potatoes are very insufficient for nutrition and also very costly, from twenty-five to fifty cents' worth giving only the value of ten cents' worth of beans. Is this sort of science of no value to the girl who is to be a housekeeper? Does it not aid in impressing on her mind all the other more abstract truths? The true value of science teaching, the knowing for certainty, the investigation for one's self, in contrast to mere belief or blind acceptance of statements, is missed in much popular teaching.

"We must awaken a spirit of investigation in our girls, as it is often awakened in our boys, but always, I think, *in spite of* the school training. We must show to the girls who are studying science in our schools that it has a very close relation to our every-day life. We must train them by it to judge for themselves, and not to do everything just as their grandmothers did. . . .

"But you are asking, what has all this to do with domestic economy? Everything, I answer, because if you train the young housekeeper to *think,* to *reason,* from the known facts to the unknown results, she will not only make a better housekeeper, but she will be a more contented one; she will find a field wide enough for all her abilities and a field almost unoccupied. The zest of intelligent experiment will add a great charm to otherwise monotonous duties. . . .

"So much for the educational side of the question. We must now consider the field itself. You will at once call to mind the great advance in the few years past in all mechanical devices which render travel comfortable, communication easy and rapid; also the great advance in metallurgy, which has given us Bessemer iron or steel, and rendered much possible that before seemed impossible. Chemistry has given us new fabrics, new dyes, and has been the right hand of metallurgy.

"We must say that of the improvements that affect our daily life, the most result from the applications of mechanics and chemistry. Now let us consider how much these have contributed to household economy. We have our carpet sweepers, knife scourers, clothes wringers, too often, alas, rendered almost useless by the ignorance of those into whose hands we put them; we have sewing machines. . . .

"Where are the fruits of chemical science? In self-raising flour, in bread powders, in washing powders, in glove cleaners, and in a hundred patent nostrums; but where are the substantial advantages commensurate with the improvements in manufacturing establishments and metallurgical works? Is housekeeping any easier, any more scientific, than it was thirty years ago? Our cooking is proverbially bad. The ventilation and drainage of many of our houses could not well be worse. Why is it? Why do not our housekeepers keep pace with our machine shops? Why do we notice such a pleasant contrast when we enter the wards of a well-ordered hospital? Why has not the knowledge of sanitary laws filtered down through the community as rapidly as the knowledge of mechanical laws? Go where you will into the country and you will find the sewing machine universal, but alas! just as poor bread, just as much fried pork, just the same open sink drain under the kitchen window, just the same damp, dark cellar, just as much fear of fresh air, as you would have found thirty years ago. And in the cities, how much better is it; rather, how much worse? The architects have learned to build houses with fewer cracks to let in air, with furnaces and no open fires, with a sort of plumbing system peculiarly sensitive to use.

"If, then, we grant, as we must, that chemical and sanitary science has not borne its due fruits in household economy, we must also grant that it must be because women have not, as yet, availed themselves of its possibilities.

"There is no place into which chemistry might not be

profitably introduced. Let us consider in what respects there is an opening for improvement. Three reasons occur to me why science should be brought into household affairs. 1st. It would benefit health. 2d. It would save labor and the wear of material. 3d. It would show us how to obtain the most for our money of the staple articles of daily consumption.

"In the first case, a few words will suffice. The housekeeper is the one person who visits all parts of the house daily. She alone is in a position to detect the first trace of the escape of sewer gas, to notice the neglected corner of the cellar, to test the cream of tartar if the biscuits come to the table yellow and alkaline, and she should know enough of science to do all this and more.

"In the second case, the saving of labor and wear of material. The management of washing is the best illustration. If we go into any grocery and ask for a cleaning soap or washing powder, an array of perhaps a dozen different kinds is spread before us, each kind claiming perfection. The cleaning soap may be eighty per cent fine sand pressed into a cake with sal-soda (washing soda). The washing powders are either crude soda with sometimes a pinch of borax, or a mixture of hard soap and washing soda. Some of the latter articles are very white hard soap with the soda, and are really very nice. But if the laundress reads the label of her washing powder and finds on it an emphasized caution against the use of sal-soda, as it injures the clothing, she naturally concludes that *this* powder is innocent of any such harmful property. Hence she uses it with unsparing hand, to the detriment of her washing.

"The third case, that of economy, will be most readily appreciated. If the housekeeper knows that she is paying twelve or fourteen cents a pound for brown soap and sal-soda, when she might purchase the same things for four or five cents, will she go on paying double price, rather than . . . to instruct her servants in the use and abuse of sal-soda?

"Perhaps the day will come when an association of housekeepers will be formed in each large town or city, with one of their number as a chemist. Some similar arrangement would be far more effective in checking adulteration than a dozen acts passed by Congress.

"The power of chemical knowledge is appreciated by manufacturers. They take advantage of every new step in science. The housekeeper must know something of chemistry in self-defense. If the dealer knows that his articles are subjected to even the simple tests possible to every woman at the head of her house, he would be far more careful to secure the best articles. Then the housekeeper should know when to be frightened.

"What an economy it would be if we could have our houses built and our utensils made on scientific principles. If women in general understood mechanical and physical laws, would they long endure the present style of architecture found even in the suburbs of Boston, which requires the coal to be shoveled down cellar only for the servants to bring up again to the kitchen range, and necessitates the carrying of the ashes down, only for somebody to bring up again? Other examples will occur to you, of ways in which labor is wasted about a house in a manner which would ruin any business or workshop. No wonder that living is so expensive. Men do not often think about these things, and it is for women to institute reforms.

"If, then, science introduced into our houses will enable us to live comfortably, if it will enable us to save in the wear and tear of furniture, to avoid great outlay of time or money in the repair of inevitable damages, to save cost on the various materials of daily use, the sum of these savings will be an amount worth considering in household economy, to say nothing of the improvement in the comfort and temper of both mistress and maids.

"The first question that will occur to any one will be, how can all this saving be accomplished? My answer is the proverbial Yankee one, another question. How have the many economies in the machine shops and metallurgical works been accomplished? . . . First, by the introduction of systematic management of every detail; second, by the employment of skilled labor.

"An English writer recently made the statement that the chief reason why the American inventions were coming upon the world with such startling rapidity and perfection was that a better class of workmen are at command here. If American *men* have been able by their perseverance, energy, and ingenuity to outstrip the world in the management of their shops, shall American women be less successful in the management of their houses?

"It is not an easy task that we have before us. We have been making great improvements in our front halls, drawing rooms, and dining rooms within the past few years, but we have not yet invaded the kitchen and pantry. We must have the careful system and the skilled labor of the shop in our kitchens before we can have the beneficial results which the shops produce.

"So long as we are content with ignorance in our kitchens, so long we shall have ignorance; but when we follow in the footsteps of our brothers and demand *knowledge,* because we know the *value of knowledge,* then we shall succeed in obtaining skilled labor . . . ; and let it not be said that American women have less energy and perseverance in their department than American men have shown in their business."

This was the first of hundreds, I might almost say thousands, of lectures that Mrs. Richards gave during the remaining years of her life. It shows how clearly she foresaw, back in the year 1879, the dangers that were to arise from the adulterations of food.

Mrs. Richards was firmly convinced, and even more firmly as time went on, that if women were finally to get control over the conditions of their own lives, a beginning must be made in childhood. She interested herself actively, therefore, in the introduction of science instruction in the public schools of Boston. The opportunity to do this came through an acquaintance which she formed in the course of the Studies at Home work with Lucretia Crocker. Miss Crocker was one of the first women to be elected a member of the Boston School Committee. She was elected in 1875, but soon afterward resigned to become Supervisor of Schools. As we have seen, she was a friend of Agassiz' and an enthusiast for the introduction of Nature Study in the schools. This enthusiasm Mrs. Richards came to share. At a time when she had a comparatively large amount of leisure, just before she was appointed instructor in Sanitary Chemistry, she made an experiment in teaching mineralogy to public school children. In this she co-operated closely with Miss Crocker. Mrs. Richards prepared the material and got together the apparatus, while Miss Crocker suggested methods of presentation. In 1884, Mrs. Richards wrote a small pamphlet called "First Lessons in Minerals," which was published by the Boston Natural History Society as a companion volume to similar treatises on plants and animals.

During the time when Mrs. Richards was teaching mineralogy, she made the interesting experiment of giving the same set of lessons to public school children and to a class of undergraduates at Harvard. The results were rather surprising, though probably not so much so to her as to others. The children trusted to their own observation instead of turning to books for their conclusions, and were able much sooner than the older pupils to identify and classify minerals.

In speaking before the Woman's Education Association about the value of scientific work for young pupils, she said, "If the only object is to make the child quick to observe, sure to remember, keen in reasoning, send him into the streets as a bootblack or a newsboy; but if we consider the moral effect as well, we shall choose the classroom.

"But we do not wish to make a dull, sullen boy where the streets would have made a wide-awake business man. When we think of the fascination of the city thoroughfare, the motion, the noise, the amusing incidents, we do not wonder that the bright boy chafes at being cooped up in a close room and made to do sums or to learn the names of the cities of Europe while the sunshiny hours are passing.

"The unwilling mind is not a teachable mind. Tasks are always irksome. How can the schoolroom be made as fascinating as the street and at the same time teach its moral lessons? If a guest in the family attempts to amuse the child with his watch, he does not say, 'I have a curious round object in my pocket with wheels inside,' etc., but he shows it and explains it as a text for what else he says.

"So, in school, the child should have some pegs driven into the wall of memory upon which he may hang a line of objects more or less distinctly comprehended, but which the association of ideas will bring out years after. Now some of us believe that the introduction into the school-room of natural objects, flowers, minerals, shells, stuffed birds, dried insects, fibers, etc., furnish these pegs upon which the facts of geography and history and the exercises in speaking and writing English may be advantageously hung. We believe that the time gained in the readiness of comprehension and clearness of ideas will more than compensate for the time taken in observing, and also that the child's innate curiosity will be wisely directed and his reading influenced."

To the development of the course in mineralogy, and also to the Teachers' School of Science conducted by the Boston Natural History Society, Mrs. Richards gave much time in the early eighties.

In 1885 came the opportunity to combine science with manual training. In this year two school kitchens were established in Boston, one by Mrs. Quincy Shaw at North Bennet Street School, and another by Mrs. Mary Hemenway at the Tennyson Street School. Two years later the latter was taken over by the School Committee, and became Boston School Kitchen No. 1, while the former remained an experiment station for working out new ideas in practical education. Mrs. Richards' hope for this kind of teaching was that it would hold its immediately practical value and gradually be transformed in a systematic course of training in applied science. Toward this she worked and preached.

In a monograph entitled, "Domestic Economy in Public Education," published in 1889 by the New York College for the Training of Teachers, she wrote:

"While sympathizing heartily in the work of the cooking schools so successfully established, the writer fears lest they come to be considered an end instead of a means, as has been the case in schools of carpentry. In a word, they should 'not teach how to make a living, but how to live.' To do this effectually, the foundation should be broadened. Just as the course in carpentering has developed into the manual training school, so should the eminently successful cooking school develop into a course in domestic economy. All the work of the schools should be in harmony, and the cooking should no longer be considered an outside affair, an interloper, a crowder-out of more important studies, but all the teachers should co-operate to make most effective the practical lesson." Significant words, considering they were spoken at a time when the world recognized only the immediate practical utility of courses in cooking, and not their broad educational value.

She was keenly appreciative of the difficulties under which the pioneer teachers of these subjects labored, and it was apparently in recognition of the very meager literature available for them that she published in 1885 her book, "Food Materials and Their Adulterations," which brought together the results of the work that had been done in the Woman's Laboratory. When Mrs. Hemenway, in 1888, started a Normal School of Household Arts, she gave the lectures on Food and Nutrition.

After Miss Crocker's death, in 1885, a strong effort was made to induce Mrs. Richards to leave her position in the Institute and become Supervisor of Schools. In a letter written about this time, she said: "I have been a little worried by an attempt to make me think it was my duty to accept the nomination to fill the vacancy made by Miss Crocker's death, on the Board of Supervisors in the Boston Schools. A political place with no power, only influence, is not to my taste." She preferred to remain outside the public school organization, free to give help and encouragement at every point, pressing workers into the service, giving them faith in their own powers, and holding before them high ideals. How significant she considered this work in the public schools is shown by a letter written to a young woman who was considering a position to teach cooking:

"We are trying to make real homes for the children of our land. We are trying to stem the tide of intemperance by giving good food; we are trying to save the resources of our country by showing how cheap food may be good food. We are right on the threshold of this work. The children are ready; the public is ready with support; we are waiting for a true philanthropic teacher to work out the best way of making it available to girls of our land. To me the question appeals so much that I am ready to make any sacrifice for it."

Chapter X

AMONG COLLEGE WOMEN

WHEN Mrs. Richards was graduated from Vassar, in 1870, college women were too few and too widely separated to have a collective influence in any community; but as women's colleges multiplied and as the size of their classes increased, the graduates grew in number and began to feel their class power. Then came the thought of increasing their influence through organization. The first associations of college women brought together the graduates of one college only. In 1871 Vassar women united themselves into the Associate Alumnæ of Vassar College, and four years later a Boston Branch of this society was formed.

"We had a breath of Vassar in the holidays," Mrs. Richards wrote in January 1876; "twenty old graduates met and founded the Boston Alumnæ Association. The main object was to awaken an active interest in Vassar's present state and to start scholarship funds so that poor but bright girls could be sure of an education."

To tell the story of what Mrs. Richards did through this organization for the girls of Vassar would be to repeat the story of what she did for the girls of the Institute of Technology. Her work was of course less direct and personal, because she was separated from them by distance, but it was based on the same broad comprehension of their needs. To provide them with scholarships, to protect their health, to broaden their opportunities, to shield them from undesirable publicity, and to bring them into public notice in helpful ways was her untiring endeavor. She "always had time for Vassar."

Her hope for Vassar students, as well as for other educated women, is expressed in a paper of hers, entitled "The College Woman in 1950":

"This young woman will have an understanding of the main forces which are man's servants, not because she is in college, but because she learned them in the elementary schools, in the fitting schools, all through her preparatory courses; for by that time it will be essential that every child shall know the world he lives in, whether he knows anything else or not.

"This young woman will not run at the sight of a cow, scream at the sound of a mouse, or get off an electric car backward (it may be that the cars will pass each other the other way by that time). She will have learned to carry bundles on her right arm.

"Instead of mental gymnastics practiced for the sake of showing mere prowess, there will be a positive power of control of mind to do what is demanded of it, but more noticeable will be the perfect control of the body and the perfect poise of the health. The college woman of 1950 will join with Maria Mitchell in being ashamed to be ill; it will be a mark of low intelligence in those days.

"I do not think she will 'do her own sewing,' as was the vogue in 1870, or even her own mending. She will know plenty of persons who can do it for a consideration and her time will bring more money. She *may* be her own milliner, for in that day more attention will be paid to the shape of bonnets and arrangement of ribbons and shades of color especially suited to the wearer and to the rest of the dress. So also the small details of the toilette will be more expressive of the individual, and therefore the individual must give thought to them.

"The well-educated young woman of 1950 will blend art and science in a way we do not dream of; the science will steady the art and the art will give charm to science.

"This young woman will marry—yes, indeed, but she will take her pick of the men, who will by that time have begun to realize what sort of men it behooves them to be.

"Each will be a center—the pin of a concretion around which will grow all society. She will not have need to resort to subterfuge before her boys. A sense of power is the most intoxicating stimulant a mortal can enjoy; power over other powerful forces, over other persons; and power used for the general good brings its own reward in satisfaction as well as pleasure—not always the same thing.

"Freedom to live out her life will bring with it a new

zest in life, a new wish to make it of service. Instead of the
vain kicking against the pricks (and how vain and how
prickly some of us could tell, with the sense of the utter
senselessness of it) there will come a radiance which will
transform the face and ennoble the expression.

"Her share of the work will be well done, carefully done,
but she will not be a slave to circumstances. A worse
slavery than the world knows embitters the lives of thousands
of women today, and they never let it be guessed because
they see no way out, and they take all kinds of petty ways
to revenge themselves.

"She will be so fair to look upon, so gentle and so quiet
in her ways, that you will not dream that she is of the same
race as the old rebels against the existing order, who, with
suspicion in our eyes and tension in our hearts, if not in our
fists, confront you now with the question, 'What are you
going to do about it?' "

In June 1894, Mrs. Richards was chosen alumna trustee
of Vassar College. At the time when she came upon the
board the question of sewage disposal was pressing. The
custom had been to throw all the sewage, with little previous
treatment, into Casperkill Creek at a point about six miles
from the Hudson River. But as time went on the authorities
of Poughkeepsie objected to this method of disposal, and the
project of building a sewer to the Hudson River was considered, at a cost which was variously estimated at from
$37,000 to $50,000. While this matter was under consideration in the trustees' meeting, Mrs. Richards, being a new
member, sat silent. Finally, when her opinion was asked,
she said that it had always seemed to her that educational
institutions should lead and not follow in the matter of
sanitation, and that for Vassar College to dispose of its
sewage by allowing it to flow into the Hudson would be
mediæval. When asked to suggest an alternative she outlined fully and from intimate knowledge of the newest and
most reliable methods a plan for a sewage disposal plant.
This plant was later installed at a cost of $7,500. But
economy was the least advantage that Mrs. Richards saw
in the plan; to her it was an opportunity to make an experiment of great value to the world, and she believed this to be

the business of every institution of advanced learning. In order to help the project along, she herself gave her professional services for many years, analyzing the drinking water of the college frequently in order to make sure that it was not being contaminated. She was proud to have a part as a graduate in what she believed to be a contribution of her college to public health.

It was not until 1882 that graduates of different colleges were brought together into one organization. That year saw the founding of the Association of Collegiate Alumnæ. Strangely enough, the idea of this organization, whose membership consisted exclusively of college women, was conceived in the mind of a woman who had not been to college. This far-sighted woman, Mrs. Emily Talbot, of Boston, was the mother of two daughters, one of whom, later Dean Marion Talbot of the University of Chicago, had just graduated from Boston University, while the other "was soon to follow out into the social world handicapped by that strange, new thing, a college education." As Mrs. Talbot looked forward into the future, she saw "an ideal organization of college women for practical educational work, a body ready to lend aid, counsel, and encouragement to all who desire to fit themselves by sound education for the duties of life," and she wanted to give her daughters to the work of founding such a society.

Of course she consulted Mrs. Richards; everyone did in educational matters. Mrs. Richards seems to have hesitated at first. Perhaps this was because the plan of work was not definitely outlined, for she always feared to set in motion the time-consuming machinery of organization except for big purposes. She was willing to make the experiment, however, and she co-operated with Miss Talbot in issuing a call for an informal meeting. This meeting, which was held on November 28, 1881, brought together seventeen women from eight different colleges and universities.

A letter written by Mrs. Richards on January 4 says: "We are starting a new project here which you will be pleased to hear about. It is a general association of college graduates. We got together at a caucus on short notice, graduates of seven or eight colleges. We are to have a meeting for organ-

izing January 14. I do not know what good will come of it,
but Mrs. Talbot, of Boston (the one who engineered the
Girls' Latin School through) suggested the idea, and as we
see no objection and some possible advantages, we are going
into it. We shall be a sort of a bureau of information, at any
rate."

On January 14 the Association of Collegiate Alumnæ[1] was
organized, at a meeting over which Mrs. Richards presided.
Efforts made to reach all the graduates in New England and
New York of the eight colleges which had been represented
at the first conference—Oberlin, Smith, Vassar, Wellesley,
Michigan, Wisconsin, Cornell, and Boston—resulted in
bringing together only sixty-five people.

Of Mrs. Talbot's influence on the association, Mrs. Richards said long afterwards: "The fact that the organzation was
successful from the start was due to the counsels of one who
had had much experience in other organizations and in
working by men's methods, for from the first it has been
characterized by cool deliberation and has been free, we
flatter ourselves, from feminine fads. To have a right start
in life is a great advantage, and our godmother saw to that.
She gave us our watchword—*Work, and practical work*. We
were not to meet for amusement nor to pass an idle hour.
She impressed upon us that where much is given much shall
be required. She called us to service in the cause of all
education—for the state and for the better life of the community."

The plan of the association was always to accept for
membership only the graduates of certain approved colleges
of high standing. To the original eight, four were added
during the first year. These were the Massachusetts Institute
of Technology, Wesleyan University at Middletown, Syra-
cuse, the University of Kansas. During Mrs. Richards' life,
Barnard, Bryn Mawr, Radcliffe, Northwestern, Leland Stan-
ford, Western Reserve, and the Universities of California,
Illinois, Chicago, Minnesota, Missouri, and Nebraska were
added, and the individual membership increased to fifty-two
hundred.

[1] Later the American Association of University Women.

The general organization was chiefly concerned with raising the standard of scholarship in colleges admitting women and with providing fellowships for advanced study in this country and abroad. The branches which were formed in forty-seven cities and towns, East and West, were interested chiefly in local educational problems. From the first Mrs. Richards was active in the work of the general association and in the Boston branch, and was welcomed as a speaker at the conventions and at the meetings of the various branches.

Dean Talbot, who, as we have seen, was with Mrs. Richards from the first in this work, says: "It was characteristic of her that after the association was successfully started she should decline to accept conspicuous official positions and should serve rather as a 'high private' wherever opportunity offered or duty called. She was, however, a director during the first year and vice-president in 1886 and 1890. As first vice-president she was in charge of the first meeting held west of New York State."

The records of the association showed that the first subject considered was the health of college students. Mrs. Richards was in part responsible for the first circular issued, which presented very clearly the low standards of the colleges in regard to physical education, and made a very strong plea for greater attention to the physical basis of college students' life. Later she prepared a leaflet, "Health in Preparatory Schools," with blanks to be filled by teachers and parents. These were widely distributed by the association, and although no statistics were compiled from the returns, there is much evidence that the pamphlet proved useful by suggesting lines of investigation which might be entered upon and improvements which might be introduced into the schools.

Soon after the organization, the need of opportunities for graduate study became apparent. Here again for many years Mrs. Richards was a constant source of inspiration. She proposed and outlined a circular on graduate study, and served several years as chairman of the committee. She was a member of the council to accredit women for advanced work in foreign universities and of the committee on a national university.

Mrs. Richards' first paper before the association was read in 1890, its subject being, "The Relation of College Women to Progress in Domestic Science." In this paper she said:

"The college-bred woman is a comparatively modern product. Twenty years ago one could almost count on one's fingers the women who were so educated and who were old enough to impress their individualities on any community. It is only just now, when there are two thousand or more mature women who have known what a college training is in their own experience, that we can begin to talk of their influence or lay out work for them as a class. As individuals, they find their own work; but in some respects it seems to me that they have obligations laid upon them as a reward or penalty for their position as pioneers, as the most observed class of the present day. We have been treated for some years to discussions from eminent men as to our mental ability, our moral and physical status, our predilection for matrimony, our fitness for voting or for the Presidency; but the kind of a home we should make if we did make one, the position we should take on the servant question, the influence we should have on the center and source of political economy, the kitchen, seem to have been ignored."

From this beginning she went on to advocate the thorough study of domestic economy in all our colleges for women, summarizing her arguments in this way: "First, and, from an educational point of view, foremost, to broaden the ideas of life with which the young woman leaves college, to bring her in touch with the great problems which press more closely each year.

"Second, to secure a solid basis for improvement. Those of us who have had a hand in reforms know how much work is wasted for want of knowing what has already been done."

In October 1911, at the first annual meeting to be held after Mrs. Richards' death, the association seriously considered the subject which she had presented to it twenty-one years before.

One of the most delicate and difficult tasks of the association was to extend the corporate membership without injustice to individual colleges, on the one hand, and without, on the other hand, lowering the standards set by the association for the very purpose of giving the weaker institutions an incentive to strengthen their courses. In the task of selection, Mrs. Richards' intimate knowledge of colleges and universities in all parts of the country came to be of great service. When she advised the acceptance or the rejection of an institution, the information which she gave the special committees was not second-hand, but was based upon intimate personal knowledge of existing conditions.. The president of one of these debated colleges wrote to an officer of the association: "The one who knows most about us has been our strongest supporter. Mrs. Ellen H. Richards has been here, and she is our friend."

Her interest, too, in educational institutions of all types and her understanding of the value of the work done by the smaller colleges, even those which were not of such grade as to permit of membership in the association, made it possible for her to make an adverse decision the opportunity for co-operation and helpfulness. The president of one of these smaller colleges said:

"I remember a characteristic interview in Mrs. Richards' study at the Institute on a day of steaming heat at the beginning of our summer vacation in 1889. We were both tired and I was in perplexity at the attitude of the Association of Collegiate Alumnæ toward our college. Mrs. Richards stood firm by the definition of a college as laid down by the association, while I contended for a much more generous interpretation, knowing, as I did, how all the germs of development in arts and sciences had existed in such institutions as mine, even before the foundations of some of the colleges in the association were laid. It is pleasant to remember how then and always we have been able to sink our differences in our desire to serve the general good. She became one of the most helpful friends our college has ever had."

Mrs. Richards' last work for the general Association of Collegiate Alumnæ was in connection with a committee on euthenics, whose work was barely outlined at the time of her death. The intention of the association had been to form a committee on eugenics, or the science of human improvement by better breeding; but because of Mrs. Richards'

urgent pleading, it decided to give its attention to the science
of controllable environment. The discussion in the association
followed the lines of a friendly controversy which had been
going on between Dr. C. B. Davenport and other scientists,
on the one hand, and Mrs. Richards, on the other, as to
whether eugenics was the parent of euthenics or *vice versa*,
the supporters of eugenics contending that the best results
for the race were to be obtained through the careful selection
of parents, Mrs. Richards that improved environment would
improve the physical condition of future parents and bring
quicker results in race development.

The activities in which the Boston branch engaged were
many, and in all of them Mrs. Richards had an active part. It
maintained for some time a Fellowship in the School of
Housekeeping connected with the Women's Educational and
Industrial Union of Boston. The Fellowship was held by
Gertrude Bigelow, and the result was the preparation of a
monograph on "The Relation of Cost in Home Cooked and
Purchased Food," which was published in 1901 as Bulletin
No. 19 of the Massachusetts Bureau of Labor. This study,
which was the first of the kind to be made in this country,
was suggested by Mrs. Richards, and was in line with her
belief that housewives should have the benefit of all the
knowledge obtainable about ways of reducing the amount of
labor involved in maintaining a home.

Another important work which Mrs. Richards did in
connection with the Boston branch was an investigation of
the sanitary condition of the public school buildings of the
city. This work was in charge of a committee of which Mrs.
Alice U. Pearmain was chairman and Mrs. Richards an
active member. The committee secured as an expert Mr.
S. Homer Woodbridge, Professor of Heating and Ventilation
at the Massachusetts Institute of Technology, and he and his
assistants made a scientific investigation of the heating and
ventilating apparatus and of the plumbing in all of the buildings used for school purposes. The cleanliness of the buildings and the provisions for exit in case of fire were also noted.
The results of this investigation it would be unfair to give here.
They form a dark chapter in the history of school administration in Boston, which has a correspondingly dark chapter

in the history of school affairs in every great city of the country. Boston, therefore, must not be singled out and made to suffer before the public because it happened to have, or was so fortunate as to have, an exceptionally enterprising and public-spirited branch of the Collegiate Alumnæ.

It is sufficient to say that the results of this investigation were very far-reaching. It served to arouse public opinion to the belief that responsibility for the condition of the schools was altogether too much divided. In 1897, a committee of citizens of which Mrs. Richards was a member started an agitation for the purpose of getting through the Legislature a bill providing for certain important changes.

Mrs. Richards prepared for this agitation by entering upon a correspondence with prominent educators in all parts of the country, and when she felt that her plans were sufficiently well laid she arranged with a committee of the Woman's Education Association, of which she was chairman, to send out invitations for a mass meeting in Huntington Hall for the purpose of considering proposed changes in the school committee. This meeting was most cleverly planned. Instead of advertising it in a general way, the committee sent invitations to members of the Legislature, city officials, superintendents of schools in all parts of New England, members of associations interested in education, and to many others. Each invitation contained a note saying that upon the receipt of an acceptance a ticket for a reserved seat would be sent. This made it possible to judge from the returns the extent and also the distribution of the interest. It served, also, to make it seem a privilege to be invited to be present. The outcome of the meeting was the appointment of a committee to prepare a bill for presentation to the Legislature the following session. This bill, as it was finally drafted after much discussion by a committee of which Mrs. Richards was a member, provided for a reduction of the school committee from twenty-four members to twelve, for placing the responsibility for all educational matters, including the selection of teachers, with the superintendent, for placing the responsibility of all financial matters with a business agent, for the creation of a school faculty to give the teachers a voice in the educational policy, and for the creation of a voluntary committee in each ward of the city to act as an intermediary between the parents and teachers.

In the rough notes which Mrs. Richards left of the speech she made during this campaign, she said in connection with the centralizing of educational authority in the superintendent: "A man can say 'No' in an hour where a committee is likely to discuss for weeks. It has been happily said that 'if the children of Israel, in their passage through the wilderness, had been governed by a committee instead of by a leader, they would probably be wandering around the wilderness today.'"

The committee having the bill in charge was convinced of the desirability of enacting the bill as a whole, but after several years of unsuccessful effort it was obliged to abandon the project. There remained no evidence of its prolonged agitation except an educated public opinion. A few years afterward a bill was passed which embodied some of the provisions for which Mrs. Richards had worked so hard. The school committee was reduced in size, not, however, to twelve, but to five members, and a schoolhouse commission was created. But the provisions which might have served to democratize school affairs—the creation of a school faculty and a citizens' committee—were not embodied. There was a widespread opinion in Boston that if they had been, much friction between the teaching force and the schools might have been averted.

The work of the Sanitary Science Club formed by the Boston branch has already been mentioned.

It would be impossible to review Mrs. Richards' work in connection with the Association of Collegiate Alumnæ without being convinced that her influence was due largely to the fact that she was more than a college woman and that she was able to bring this organization into connection with other and varied activities and broader interests. Someone has spoken recently of the "cross fertilization" of the sciences. A "cross fertilization" of good works was always going on where Mrs. Richards was involved. To illustrate: Her travels in connection with Professor Richards' work as a mining engineer carried her often into the Southern States and had familiarized her with its educational problems. She saw a need there of an organization similar to the Collegiate Alumnæ Association, and when, in 1902, such an organization was formed, she was not content to look on, but became one of its most earnest and helpful members. The Southern Association of College Women included the graduates of many Northern colleges, but almost without exception they were residents of the South; and Mrs. Richards was one of the very few Northern women who saw the chance to give the newer society the benefit of the experience of the older organization. The catholicity of her interests was never more apparent than when, at the jubilee celebration at the twenty-fifth anniversary of the founding of the Association of Collegiate Alumnæ, she, a New England woman by birth and training, offered the greetings of the Southern Association of College Women.

She was always interested in creating for women opportunities for advanced work. She had an important part in the founding of the Hyannis Marine Laboratory, which later became the Woods Hole Laboratory, and she was actively interested in the association which was formed for the purpose of securing entrance for women into Johns Hopkins Medical College. In 1898 she became one of the charter members of the Naples Table Association for Promoting Laboratory Research by Women.

The history of the Naples Table Association, like that of the Association of Collegiate Alumnæ, is of interest here only as it shows a phase of her untiring labors. In the spring of 1898, a small group of women gathered in Cambridge to discuss the formation of a society to support a table for American women at the zoological station in Naples. This station had been founded in 1872 by Professor Anton Dohrn, then of Jena, for the purpose of doing something of lasting benefit for the science which he loved. He had already opened, at his own expense, a small laboratory at Messina, but this was but the incentive to greater things. Dedicating his own private fortune to the enterprise, winning the interest of leading scientists, securing substantial aid from European governments, he persevered until his dream became a reality. On the shore of the beautiful Bay of Naples rose the white marble building of the *Stazione Zoölogica di Napoli*.

From the first, Dr. Dohrn admitted women to the station on equal terms with men; and when the scientists of the world were uniting to celebrate the twenty-fifth anniversary of the station, the suggestion came from Dr. Ida Hyde, who had enjoyed the privileges of the station, that American women show their appreciation of the position he had taken with regard to women students by annually contributing to its support.

The organization was completed in April 1898, and from the outset Mrs. Richards was an interested and valued member. "Much that she did for the work," one of her associates says, "no one could have done better, much of it no one else could have done at all. She saw what ought to be done and could be done, and she saw how to do it. The work of the Naples Table was peculiarly congenial to her, and she was naturally consulted on every detail of the organization and scope. This association had the unusual distinction of an income larger than its needs, and it was decided to offer a prize of one thousand dollars for an original paper of high grade embodying the results of research in certain fields. Mrs. Richards was chairman of this committee on award from the first, and to her more than to any one is due the remarkable success of the competition. She knew the field and the workers in science so well that it was possible for her to appeal personally to the men of science and the teachers whom it was necessary to interest. They, on the other hand, had perfect confidence in her wisdom and her sanity of judgment, and they were willing and glad to help.

"To Mrs. Richards were intrusted the theses presented for competition. How zealously she guarded them! She, better than any one else on the committee, could appreciate the labor that had gone into them, and she handled those pages of typewritten matter and carefully prepared drawings almost with love. When it was necessary to submit them to the decision of the board of examiners, Mrs. Richards often personally carried the papers to the study door or even to the very office desk of the busy professor who was to pass judgment upon them. The very last work she did for this association was in connection with the essays submitted for the fifth prize to be awarded at the annual meeting in April 1911.

Even at the time of her death some of the seventeen essays submitted in competition were locked in her safe, while careful memoranda showed in whose hands others had been placed for examination." Before the time for the meeting arrived, Mrs. Richards' life had come to a close. The meeting, therefore, took the form of a memorial to her, and the following resolution was passed:

Voted, That "this Association express its appreciation of the devoted service of Mrs. Richards as the continuous chairman of the prize committee since its formation in 1900, by naming its prize in her honor the Ellen Richards Research Prize."

Chapter XI

MISSIONARY OF SCIENCE

IN JANUARY 1890, Mrs. Richards entered upon an undertaking which, to use the words of a popular English writer, was "an interesting failure, but a failure which had all the educational value of a first reconnaissance into unexplored territory." This experiment was the famous New England Kitchen of Boston, and the "unexplored territory" was the willingness of the poor to be scientifically fed.

The opportunity to make this experiment came through a somewhat remarkable and a most happy combination of circumstances. The first was the gift of a large sum of money by Mrs. Quincy Shaw, of Boston, Louis Agassiz' daughter, for the purpose of "making a thorough study of the food and nutrition of working men and its possible relation to the question of the use of intoxicating liquors." Mrs. Shaw selected Mrs. Richards to make the study, leaving the character of the investigation and of the practical work to be determined by her. She did not try to dictate as to the scope of the experiment or as to the manner in which it was to be carried on. She supplied the money and left Mrs. Richards to do the work.

A second event which led indirectly to the establishment of the New England Kitchen was an offer made in 1888 by Henry Lomb, of the Bausch and Lomb Optical Company, through the American Public Health Association, of a five hundred dollar prize for the best essay on "sanitary and economic cooking adapted to persons of moderate and small means." Seventy essays were submitted in competition for the prize, and Mrs. Richards was a member of the committee of award. The essay on "The Five Food Principles Illustrated by Practical Recipes" was found to be "not only pre-eminently the best of the seventy, but also an admirable treatise on the subject. It is simple and lucid in statement," the report went on to say, "methodical in arrangement and well adapted to the practical wants of the class to which it is addressed. Whoever may read it can have confidence in the soundness of its teachings and cannot fail to be instructed in the art of cooking by its plain precepts, founded as they are upon the correct application of the scientific principles of chemistry and physiology to the proper preparation of food for man."

The following year, at a meeting of the American Public Health Association in Brooklyn, Mrs. Richards met the writer of this paper, Mrs. Mary Hinman Abel, who had just returned from a residence of several years in Europe. In speaking, many years afterwards, of Mrs. Richards' relation to people in general, Mrs. Abel said: "I think she was always attended by the joy of possible discoveries of people. Any hour might come the great adventure." Looking back to that meeting in Brooklyn and to its consequences, we feel that Mrs. Richards must have recognized "the great adventure," for she lost no time in persuading Mrs. Abel to join her, and there was thus secured for the New England Kitchen, in its first half-year, the benefit of the thorough knowledge of the *Volks Küche, Fourneau Economique,* and other forms of public kitchens which Mrs. Abel had gained during the years spent in Europe.

A third circumstance leading to the opening of the Kitchen was an invention by Edward Atkinson of the Aladdin Oven, a device by which he hoped to revolutionize culinary methods and greatly decrease the cost of preparing food. Mr. Atkinson, as we have seen, had availed himself of Mrs. Richards' services long before, by making her consulting chemist for companies with which he was connected. When, therefore, he wished to have his new oven tested, it was natural that he should have turned to her. Though this oven was not the only cooker tested in the Kitchen, it became of great value in the preparation of the cheaper cuts of meat and of many other low-priced foods which require long, slow cooking.

Mr. Atkinson's interest in the New England Kitchen, however, was valuable chiefly for the enthusiasm which he injected into the work because of his zeal for solving some of the economic problems connected with food, and also because he was able, through his business relations with wealthy men, to secure large sums of money for experimental work.

Under auspicious circumstances, therefore, unhampered by lack of funds and having the benefit and advice of many specialists, the New England Kitchen was opened at 142 Pleasant Street, Boston, on January 1, 1890, with Mrs. Abel in immediate charge. From the beginning an attempt was made to serve cooked food for home consumption and to give the largest possible amount of nourishment for a given amount of money. In order to do this, it was necessary to take into account all available knowledge concerning the composition of foods, current prices, and possible methods of applying heat in cookery. Those who were connected with the work hoped to be able to work out recipes for a few standard foods so exactly that the food value of a given weight of the finished product would always be the same. Dr. Drown, Professor of Chemistry in the Institute of Technology, had said that if one food, beef broth for example, could be made of the same flavor and strength day after day and as unvarying in its constituents as the medicine compounded to meet a physician's prescription, that result alone would justify the proposed expenditure of time and money. By the help of repeated chemical analyses the methods of preparing this dish were brought to such perfection that the result was a food which differed only in slight degree from day to day and which had very nearly the same composition as milk without fat. It was welcomed by the physicians of Boston, and the New England Kitchen, which had been founded for the purpose of helping the poor working man, had its first triumph in meeting the needs of the well-to-do sick.

After a long series of studies, the following foods were placed on sale by weight or measure: beef broth, vegetable soup, pea soup, corn meal mush, boiled hominy, oatmeal mush, pressed beef, beef stew, fish chowder, tomato soup, Indian pudding, rice pudding, and oatmeal cakes. These foods were intended to supplement those prepared in the homes of the people. The restaurant which was later opened was not a part of the original plan.

From the beginning every part of the New England Kit-

chen was open to the public, in order that its methods might
be demonstrated and that its cleanliness might serve as an
example. In this connection it is interesting to note that,
twenty years later, there was a movement among people who
realized the menace of dirty restaurants to make it obliga-
tory for restaurant keepers to disclose their kitchens to the
public by having transparent partitions between them and the
dining rooms, or in some similar way.

Through Mr. Atkinson a grant of three hundred dollars
had been obtained for the Kitchen from the trustees of the
Elizabeth Thompson Fund. This money was used in the
purchase of scientific instruments and to pay for the frequent
chemical analyses necessary in the course of the work. The
report made by Mrs. Richards and Mrs. Abel to the trustees
of this fund was presented by Mr. Atkinson at a meeting of
the Association for the Advancement of Science in August
1890, and may be found in the published proceedings
(Volume 39).

Other kitchens after the model of the original were established in the West and North Ends of Boston, at Olneyville,
a suburb of Providence, Rhode Island, at 341 Hudson
Street, New York, and at Hull House, Chicago. They were
all failures as far as their original purpose, that of persuading
the poor of the advantage of low-priced and nourishing food,
was concerned. "Their death knell was sounded," to quote
Mrs. Richards, "by the woman who said, 'I don't want to
eat what's good for me; I'd ruther eat what I'd ruther.' " The
man, too, from Southern Europe who defiantly said, "You
needn't try to make a Yankee of me by making me eat that,"
pointing to the baked Indian pudding, may have helped to
ring the knell.

But to say that the New England Kitchen was a failure in
any broad sense would be absurd, for either one alone of
two important outgrowths, the Rumford Kitchen at the
World's Fair at Chicago, an epoch-making educational experiment, and the school lunch project in Boston and elsewhere, disprove such a statement.

The Rumford Kitchen, which was a part of the Massachusetts State exhibit at the Fair, was planned and carried on
by Mrs. Richards. In a tiny building near the south end of

the great exhibition grounds she established a model kitchen, which, like its prototype in Boston, laid bare all its processes to the public. Here, day after day, it was possible for visitors to the Fair to buy lunches whose food value had been carefully computed and noted on the bills of fare. The following is a sample menu:

			FOOD VALUE IN GRAMS			
			Proteid	Fat	Carbo-hydrates	Calories
Voit's Standard. One-quarter of one day's ration.............			24.5	14.0	125.0	742.0
Atwater's Standard. One-quarter of one day's ration...........			31.2	31.2	114.0	882.0
	Ounces	Grams				
Baked Beans...	8.4	238.1				
Brown Bread..	4.2	119.1				
One Roll......	2.0	56.7	26.3	35.6	131.4	979.3
Butter.........	0.7	19.8				
Apple Sauce...	5.3	150.2				

After the close of the World's Fair, Mrs. Richards reported to the managers: "The intention of the exhibit was to illustrate the present state of knowledge in regard to the composition of materials for human food, the means of making these materials most available for nutrition, and the quantity of each necessary for a working ration. It was also in part intended as a centennial celebration of the services to humanity of a man of Massachusetts birth and parentage, Benjamin Thompson, Count Rumford of Bavaria, the first to apply the term 'science of nutrition' to the study of human food, and the first to apply science to the preparation of food materials.

"Not the least valuable part of the exhibit consisted in the series of pamphlets prepared for the Rumford Kitchen by authorities in the several departments of science which relate to human food and nutrition. That such men as Professors Remsen, Howell, and Abel of Johns Hopkins University, Professor Chittenden of Yale University, Professor Sedgwick of the Institute of Technology, and others, were willing to prepare these scientific papers shows a great step toward placing this branch of sanitary science in its rightful place.

"This series is not yet complete, though it will finally appear in book form as a permanent result of the Chicago Exposition. [The papers were published in 1899 under the title, "Rumford Kitchen Leaflets." The copyright was in Mrs. Richards' name.] The charts, diagrams, and books of the exhibit were studied with great eagerness, and cannot but have given impetus to the investigations in these directions; while the practical outcome of the taste and relish of the food served was shown in the fact that some ten thousand people were served during the two months that the Kitchen was open, between the hours of twelve and two only, in a space so small as to permit only thirty people to be seated at the same time.

"In order to emphasize the facts above narrated, the food was served in portions containing a definite amount of nutrition, and the menu card on each table gave the requirement for one-quarter of the day's ration, with the weight and composition of each dish composing the meal. A choice of two or three luncheons, for which the price was thirty cents, was given each day, each containing three or four dishes, though an extra price was made for a glass of milk, for a cup of cocoa, tea, or coffee."

There never was so unique a lunchroom, never one which provoked so much intelligent discussion. The walls were hung with charts showing the composition of foods. The exhibits included a set of blocks demonstrating the chemical composition of the human body, a miniature chemical laboratory for housewives, and a reference library on foods and hygiene. Around the top of the wall ran a frieze of legends including, among others, the following:

"Nothing is so disgraceful to society and individuals as unmeaning wastefulness."—*Rumford*.

"The seat of courage is in the stomach."

"Preserve and treat your food as you would your body, remembering that in time food will be your body."—*B. W. Richardson*.

"A man too busy to take care of his health is like a mechanic too busy to take care of his tools."

"The spirit of each dish, and zest of all,
Is what ingenious cooks the relish call."

"Prayer and provender delay no man's journey."

"A man is what he eats."

"It is an irritating, nay a deeply saddening, problem for a wise dyspeptic to ponder, the superabundance of things cookable in this world of ours, and the extreme rarity of cooks."—*Maartens*.

"There is no pain like the pain of a new idea."—*Bagehot*.

"The scientific aspect of food must be united in bonds of holy matrimony with a practical knowledge of the cook's art, before a man can discourse learnedly of food."—*Fothergill*.

"Courage, cheerfulness, and a desire to work depends mostly on good nutrition."

It is hardly necessary to add that, with crowds of sight-seers passing through the building at all hours of the day, life was not without its amusing and entertaining incidents. The weary excursionist asked to be given something for "tired leg muscles." The literal-minded man insisted on being told the exact meaning of "There is no pain like the pain of a new idea." The uncompromising reformer read, "A man is what he eats," and wanted "more often what he drinks," added on to it. The family man complained that carbohydrates were expensive at thirty cents apiece when you had four or five children to feed. The domestic woman insisted on seeing Mrs. Rumford, and the jocular youth said in departing after lunch, "I am going right over now to get weighed and see if I really ate the twenty ounces I was entitled to by the bill of fare."

One day a representative of a scientific publication, after examining the exhibit and taking lunch, expressed satisfaction that for the first time in his life he had been scientifically fed. The following day he returned to say that, while dining the evening before, he had mentioned the Rumford Kitchen to a lady who sat beside him. Thinking she would be interested in some of its scientific aspects, he told her about the bills of fare, saying that "one could see from them the amount of carbohydrates and proteids in the food, and also its value in calories." The lady interrupted to say that she knew those things were found in food by the aid of the microscope, but for her part she would prefer not to know she was eating them.

But it all sank into the public mind, and all the more deeply because the public mind was quite empty of such information and ready to absorb. The Rumford Kitchen was the first attempt to demonstrate by simple methods to the people in general the meaning of the terms, proteids, carbohydrates, calories, and the fact that there are scientific principles underlying nutrition. At a time when laymen knew almost nothing as to the composition of food, and about foods in their relation to the human body, this enterprise laid the foundation for knowledge which we now consider almost as fundamental to a general education as the "three R's."

But a still more important outgrowth of the New England Kitchen was a plan for serving school lunches in Boston. Up to the year 1894, the privilege of serving food to the high school children of the city had been given to the school janitors, who found it a valuable perquisite. The janitors knew little, as a rule, about the science of nutrition, and the time came when it seemed wise to place the matter of school lunches in other hands. Looking about for some one to take charge, the School Committee entered into negotiations with the New England Kitchen with a view to having food sent out to various schools from this as a central plant. But this involved a large outlay of money, and again a public-spirited person with confidence in Mrs. Richards came to her aid. Mrs. William V. Kellen gave the money required for buying the apparatus necessary for the new work, and the experiment of sending out lunches began. The revolution, of course, was not effected without difficulties, and when the New England Kitchen undertook the task it entered upon troublous times. The janitors were, many of them, naturally displeased and loath to give the help and co-operation which were almost indispensable. Then, too, the School Committee, for some reason, was unwilling to have the experiment begin in one school only, but insisted that it should be made in all or none. Never was there such quick action needed, never such pressing of available workers into the service. The rooms provided were, as a rule, in the basement and inconvenient, and the time allowed for serving the lunches very short. Shops in the neighborhood of the schools tried to hold on to their trade by posting such signs as this, "Here you can get what you want to eat, and not what the School Committee says you must." But success came in the end, and the later New England Kitchen, which though under entirely different management, that of the Women's Educational and Industrial Union, was a direct outgrowth of the old, and served lunches to about five thousand high school pupils daily.

As a result of this experience and pioneer work, Mrs. Richards became an authority on school lunches, and was consulted on the subject by school superintendents and others interested in education in all parts of the country. It was at her suggestion that the Bulletin of the United States Bureau of Education, "The Daily Meals of School Children," was written, and her little pamphlet, "Good Luncheons for Rural Schools without a Kitchen," had a wide circulation and was of good service to country schools.

As a result, too, of her work in the New England and Rumford Kitchens, Mrs. Richards was consulted with reference to the diet in a very large number of institutions, hospitals, insane asylums, and schools. In some cases she took actual charge, in order to learn conditions and suggest changes. In this work she had the co-operation of Sarah E. Wentworth, who had succeeded Mrs. Abel in charge of the New England Kitchen. She was continually asked to recommend experts in food, and it was largely through her influence that positions of dignity for educated women in connection with the preparation of foods in institutions were created and the new profession of "dietitian" developed. Her office became a veritable bureau of information on the subject.

In consequence, too, of her work in the New England and Rumford Kitchens, Mrs. Richards became connected with the nutrition investigations of the United States Department of Agriculture. In 1887, the passage by Congress of the Hatch Act made possible the establishment of an agricultural experiment station in each state and territory, and the establishment of the Office of Experiment Stations in the Department of Agriculture, as a central agency for promoting the interests of the experiment stations, quite naturally followed. Professor W. O. Atwater, who had worked very effectively for the whole movement, was made first director of this central office.

Professor Atwater had long been interested in the study of problems of human nutrition by experimental methods, and believed that such work should be fostered by the federal government—a project which enlisted the sympathies and support of broad-minded men and women, and which culminated in 1894 in the establishment of the nutrition investigations of the Office of Experiment Stations of the Department of Agriculture, with funds specially appropriated by Congress for the purpose. Of this enterprise Professor Atwater, as director of the Office of Experiment Stations, was given charge.

In this same year (1894) Mrs. Richards, with Mr. Atkinson, prepared, at Professor Atwater's request, a pamphlet, "Suggestions Regarding the Cooking of Food," published by the Department of Agriculture (Mrs. Richards' contribution being a discussion of "The Nutritive Value of Common Food Materials"), which, although it was not issued as one of the then recently established series of Farmers' Bulletins, was like them in its scope, and may be fairly classed as one of the first of the popular bulletins of the Department of Agriculture on nutrition which have become such an important factor in public education.

The first technical bulletin issued as a result of the nutrition investigations of the Department of Agriculture (Bulletin 21 of the Office of Experiment Stations) was entitled, "Methods and Results of Investigations on the Chemistry and Economy of Food," and contained as one of its important sections a summary of investigations by Mrs. Richards and Mrs. Abel which have to do with the essentials for good cooking apparatus, the cookery of meat, the composition of beef, beef tea, etc., pea soup, and the keeping qualities of broth. The data summarized are taken from the reports of Mrs.

Richards and Mrs. Abel to the Trustees of the Elizabeth Thompson Fund, who in 1889 to 1890 had made a grant from this fund for experiments upon cooking which was supplemented by private gifts for the same purpose.

Other work by Mrs. Richards, which appears in publications of the Office of Experiment Stations, is a paper entitled, "Dietary Studies in Philadelphia and Chicago, 1892-1893," with Amelia Shapleigh as joint author. This paper reported the results of observations as to the food consumption and dietary customs of families with small incomes living in thickly congested districts, the observations having been made at the instance of the College Settlement Association, the primary purpose being "to obtain reliable information regarding the diet of the people of those regions, which could be used in the efforts to help them to improve their material condition."

Probably the greatest antagonism which Mrs. Richards aroused in the course of her life was in connection with her efforts to improve the quality of food served in public institutions, educational and philanthropic, and to make the diet contribute to efficiency. Her attitude is easy to understand. She saw that an enormous fraction of available human energy was being used in raising, transporting, preparing, and serving food, and it seemed to her intolerable that, after its preparation had cost so much, food should again take a great toll from the people in sickness and in wasted and inefficient lives. In her own case she studied carefully the relation of food to working power. It is said that once when she was staying at a seacoast resort and apparently enjoying a few days of rest after a summer full of very engrossing work, she came down to breakfast one morning in a very resolute way, saying, much to the surprise of her friends, that she had been making a pig of herself. "I have just been living for the moment and eating what I liked rather than what was good for me. Now I shall confine myself entirely to the proper food for brain work, and I shall set myself to writing the paper that I ought to have been at work upon, and shall make myself do it in half the time that I should have given to it, to make up for my days of idleness."

No wonder that with this strict discipline of self she should have been impatient at the sight of so much suffering caused by careless, haphazard ways of eating. She saw that the time must come when the problems of nutrition and food will be reduced to scientific principles, when people will use their food supply with intelligence, and will regulate diet and other living conditions in order to maintain the highest efficiency in work. She understood, as well as other people, that the time had not arrived, but she knew that it could be hastened if all the people would work together, some in laboratories, some preparing foods, and all making careful studies of the relation of their food to the amount of work they were able to do. A college lunchroom, for example, which strove merely to appeal to the palate fell far short of her ideal. She wished it to be an experiment station. But being greatly ahead of her times, she needed constantly to be reminded that the world in general moved slowly—very much more slowly in its thought and in its practice than she did—and that in reality the college lunchroom which had reached the point of supplying palatable food attractively served is far ahead of its time.

It was never, however, the time spent in making food attractive or palatable that troubled her, but rather the fact that people were content to stop at this point, and to have so small a fraction of the energy to which she believed they were entitled, and to do so small a part of the work which they might do toward making the world better. In lecturing on foods, she once looked up from her paper to say: "Do I not hear a whisper running from one to another of you, 'All this new-fangled talk is very well to preach for effect, but I have always eaten just what I wanted to, and I am still alive'? True, since you are here before me, but have you accomplished all in life that you might have accomplished, have you had each day your full share of heat units converted into energy, do you know what it is to be full of health and life?"

In 1899 she wrote to a woman who was greatly interested in the problems of institutional management: "I believe the greatest need of intelligent persons today is a right attitude of mind towards food and its importance to the development of the highest powers of the human race. I believe, with Professor S. H. Patten, that the well-to-do classes are being eliminated by their diet, to the detriment of social progress, and *they* and *not* the poor are the most in need of missionary work. This right attitude of mind will not be gained so long as schools, colleges, and universities continue to ignore the function of the body in providing the machinery for the mind to use. At present it is like putting a highly trained engineer into a mill with rusty and antiquated apparatus, and then blaming him for not turning out good products. As I have been saying to college audiences all winter, I believe that one year out of the four could be saved if students knew how to make the most of themselves, but there is no one to teach them. I hold the colleges guilty that they have not seized upon the knowledge already at hand and applied it, in the way of physical training and education, instead of pursuing the present plan of cruelty to animals in urging on, at the point of the bayonet as it were, a mind housed in an under-nourished body, which will have its revenge. For I believe that education alone will bring the food question from the dark, secluded corners of life to the sunlight of right thinking, and therefore I am bending all my energies toward public school teaching of the right sort. Meanwhile I am waiting for the authorities of some college to show that they are up-to-date and are willing to put the food department on a level with the Greek or mathematics, by appointing a professor of Hygiene and Sanitation and teaching the student the value of a sound body as well as of a bright mind."

At another time she said, in words which leave little room for misunderstanding, "In the twentieth century it will be held a criminal offense for a college to lure students to its halls under the pretense of education, and then slowly poison them by bad air and poor food."

It is evident from the story of the New England and Rumford Kitchens and of the serving of school lunches that Mrs. Richards early allowed her philanthropic and altruistic interests to call her away from the pursuit of pure science. For this she was frequently citicized; but she, on the other hand, had her own criticisms to make. She once said: "The sanitary research worker in the laboratory and field has gone nearly to the limit of his value. He will soon be smothered in his own work if no one takes it." She wanted to make applications of the knowledge he was turning out to every problem of human life. Of herself she said, "Research has to step one side when I feel the pressure of sociologic progress."

It is doubtful if she was ever out of sympathy intellectually with the painstaking methods of pure science, though she was temperamentally unsuited for the routine details of such work herself. There were times, however, when with her clear understanding of pressing needs she manifested some impatience with the slowness of scientifically trained people to make application of known facts. She seems to have had before her always, on the one hand, the vision of a world full of sickness and suffering, and of a people failing, because of preventable ills, to reach their highest efficiency and greatest usefulness; and on the other, a great mass of knowledge and facts which, if they could be properly used and applied, would serve to relieve the suffering and prevent this waste of energy. She saw the need of a chain of workers extending from the laboratory to the people, and she was ready and anxious to find and keep her place in the chain. If others had found their places and had filled them as unselfishly and as toilfully as she did, there would have been no gaps in the chain, no failure of science to serve humanity.

Chapter XII

IN JOURNEYINGS OFTEN

EVENTS were now fast leading up to the organization of the home economics movement, which may be considered the crowning labor of Mrs. Richards' life, because it brought together her numberless lines of work and directed them toward a well-defined end—education for right living. In the perfect foundation which she had been laying, though unconsciously, for leadership in this movement, travel as well as work had had a part. For this reason there have been brought together in Appendix B extracts from letters which she wrote on journeys taken during the period when the many activities described in the previous chapters were being carried on. Fortunately these letters show not only how wide an acquaintance with people and with social and educational movements she brought to her later labors, but also her keen enjoyment of travel. They reveal, therefore, her serious purposes and also herself, with all her boundless joy in living.

In speaking of her journeyings she once said that she had traveled "only as each year had brought its special investigations." She seldom went to a place because it was a popular resort or because it contained things beautiful or interesting to see, but almost always in connection with some special work either of her own or of Professor Richards'. Arrived, she saw more than most people see, for she had eyes for its geological formation and its minerals, its meteorological conditions, its trees and flowers in their botanical relations as well as in their beauty, its water supply, its peculiar sanitary problems, its engineering projects, and its educational advancement. To follow her travels, therefore, is to follow her in her labors, her interests, and her thought.

During the vacations of 1872 and 1873, while she was a student at the Institute of Technology, she took journeys which in her early enthusiasm she called "scientific expeditions." The first was to the St. Lawrence River country and the second to Nova Scotia.

GOUVERNEUR, NEW YORK,
August 5, 1872.

You will wonder how I came here. . . . With the teacher of mineralogy in the Girls' High School, Boston, I have been attempting a scientific vacation—not at all rivalling Agassiz, you know, for it's only "two women," but just to see whether "two women" could do anything. We say, now on the eve of our departure for home, "Yes, they can." We have been four weeks in Maine, Canada, New York—visiting the mineral locations, obtaining specimens and studying them in their native beds. We have visited *alone* lead, copper, tin, silver, gold and iron mines, been courteously treated by all, not tenderly as ladies, but no one has put a bar in our way. We have taken a horse and driven about from place to place with hammer and chisel and botany press, etc. The experiment seems a perfect success—we are strong and black as gypsies—being out of doors all the time.

The following year she made a scientific pilgrimage. In July, 1874, in company again with Miss Capen, she went to Northumberland, Pennsylvania, where Joseph Priestley is buried, the occasion being a Chemical Centennial in honor of the one hundredth anniversary of the discovery of oxygen.

In 1875 occurred her marriage to Professor Richards and the unique wedding trip with his class in mining engineering.

In 1876 she went abroad with Professor Richards, chiefly for the purpose of visiting laboratories, mines, and smelting works, and buying chemical apparatus for the Woman's Laboratory.

No letters written from the Centennial Exhibition [Philadelphia, 1876] have been found; but years after she visited it, Mrs. Richards said in a little leaflet entitled, "Exhibits and the Home Economics Movement": "To the casual onlooker the growth of the domestic science cult may seem to have been fortuitous or spasmodic or sporadic even, but there is a distinct trail back to the Philadelphia Exposition of 1876, when America was awakened to its own deficiencies in the culinary art, and in house furnishing and decoration among other things. These deficiencies clearly indicated the necessity for a wider knowledge of science in household management. The manual training idea, developed from the work of Russia and Sweden shown at this exposition, gave impetus and opportunity to American adaptation. Many lines of progress started in this world exposition of 1876."

In 1873 Miss Swallow had joined the American Association for the Advancement of Science (A_3S she used to write it for short), and in 1877 she was elected a fellow. From that time on, many of her trips were to its annual meetings.

During the summers of 1881 and 1882 she worked with Professor Richards in Northern Michigan.

In 1883 she went with Professor Richards to Virginia, where he was holding a movable School of Mines. That year she went ahead of the party and arranged its itinerary.

In 1884, after her appointment as Instructor in Sanitary Chemistry, Mrs. Richards made a trip to England for the purpose of attending the International Health Exhibition at South Kensington and to get material which would be of service to her in her work. She was accompanied on this trip by Alice Palmer, who had been one of the first students in the Woman's Laboratory. After attending the exhibition they made a trip to the Land of the Midnight Sun, which Mrs. Richards had long looked forward to visiting. This was probably the only place she ever visited in her life where the days had enough hours to suit her.

The letters which she wrote about the exhibition and the conferences are not to be found, and very unfortunately, for she made constant references to this visit in later years, and it seems in many ways to have marked an advance in her thought. Years later she wrote: "I do hope the Chicago exposition can make a good showing in the educational line, for I have such vivid recollections of the excellence of the educational side of the London Health Exposition in 1884 that I know how much we have to do to surpass that. It has been my inspiration ever since. I do not believe a school in America can make such a showing of Domestic Economy as that in Belgium, nor a Normal School surpass that of Tokyo, Japan." And again: "In England, in 1884, I saw young men from the universities in the Board Schools giving instruction as to babies' milk. In America we have allowed the newspapers and the magazines to give the public instruction that belongs to universities."

Repeatedly during a trip to California in 1885 (see letter on page 202), she made reference to the strain upon Professor Richards of the traveling and of the work. The fact is that for many years he had been working at too high pressure. Between 1878 and 1883, years of financial depression for the Institute, he had not only directed the work of his own department, but filled the office of secretary, and when he gave up this extra work it was only to be faced by large arrears in his own professional labors. For years he was in low physical condition, and the crisis came in the fall of 1886, when he had a long and serious siege of typhoid pneumonia.

For several years after this, Mrs. Richards seems to have contented herself with short trips. Professor Richards' sickness and long convalescence, the sanitary survey which was then in progress, a fall on the rocks at the seashore which partially disabled her for a long time, her mother's declining health, and the great pressure of work connected with the New England Kitchen and the School Lunches combined to prevent her from going far from home. This was the time, too, when she was finding joy and recreation with her beautiful Duchess, the horse for which she had an affection that in a weaker woman of fewer interests might have seemed unreasonable. A few weeks after Duchess died, she wrote: "It has been a delightfully warm, sunny day, but no longer do such days bring me pleasure. Since my beautiful Duchess went to the land of perpetual sunshine I would rather it rained. I never have been for a drive or walk even over the old roads."

In August, 1888, Mrs. Richards and Marion Talbot took a carriage trip through the White Mountains, during which Mrs. Richards selected a site for a summer cottage at Randolph, New Hampshire. Her account of this journey written to Professor Richards was in the form of a narrative entitled, "The Adventures of Black Billy in the White Mountains," and was supposedly written by the horse which she drove. At the point, however, where "Madame and Mademoiselle," the two strange women traveling alone, chose to climb mountains, Black Billy was dependent upon Bruce, the collie, for information. Bruce reported:

"A preliminary trial of strength was made by ascending Randolph Hill by a path through the woods one and one-half miles and then descending by the road three miles. Madam selected a house lot on the Hill and she declared she had never seen so fine a view of the mountains." [Mrs. Richards bought the house lot referred to, but did not see it again until 1904, when she built on it a cottage which she named "The Balsams."]

"At 6 o'clock on Wednesday morning the party started for the Mount Adams trip. The trail, for that is all the so-called path is, at first runs through a meadow across Moose river, on stepping stones, then through heavy woods where considerable logging has been done so that the guide could not find his own path. But after climbing through many fallen trees and wading several bogs, a more solid ground was reached. Then every step *was up*. Four thousand feet in four miles means a rise at every foot, some of the way steeper than old-fashioned back stairs. Madam with her 155 pounds weight to carry took frequent occasions to admire the trees and moss and abundant Spring flowers when there was no view to exclaim over or no spring of clear, cold water to test.

"Four hours brought the party out to a rock where there were low trees and alpine flowers but nothing to obstruct the view. Fortunately clouds tempered the heat of the sun without cutting off a view of the landscape. Specimens of plants had to be gathered and 12 o'clock found the party camped for luncheon at the foot of an immense snow bank which furnished a small river of cool water.

". . . The sharp, stony peak looked a great way off. A sharp scramble, however, conquered and on the topmost stone the eye commanded a view not to be forgotten. The day was a perfect success, a delight to all."

The summer of 1893 and much of the following autumn she spent at the World's Fair, superintending the work of the Rumford Kitchen. The Fair itself she described in Whitmanesque fashion as a "most wonderful exhibition of American brag, courage, and persistence—a grand scene—

art—architecture—in fact, everything good and everything bad at the same time."

During the last fifteen years of her life, she traveled increasingly, but almost invariably her journeyings were for the purpose of lecturing or of attending conventions or committee meetings. In 1886 she had added the American Public Health Association, and about the same time the National Educational Association, to the list of societies whose conventions she faithfully attended, and in 1899 she started the Lake Placid Conference. The expenditure of money and of time involved in these journeys was enormous. What others spend in pleasure trips she spent in seeking the fellowship of people of kindred minds and purposes, in this way demonstrating the strength of her interest and faith in the organizations to which she had given her allegiance.

Chapter XIII

LAKE PLACID CONFERENCE

THIS record, necessarily incomplete, and probably further from complete than even those realize who are most familiar with her work, will serve to show the discipline, the experience, the knowledge, the training, the acquaintance with people and with organizations which Mrs. Richards brought to the organized home economics movement which had its beginning in the first Lake Placid Conference of Home Economics, held in 1899.

In reviewing the work of the Lake Placid Conference, she once said, "The movement took rise in the same realization of 'the inconvenience of ignorance' that led John Eliot, the Apostle to the Indians, to found a school in 1690 'to do away with it.' " The form of ignorance which in 1899 had grown so inconvenient as to call for a united effort to "do away with it" was in connection with household administration under the new conditions which great social and industrial changes had brought. "The flow of industry had passed on and had left idle the loom in the attic, the soap kettle in the shed." The form of the home was being gradually but surely changed, not, however, because of intelligent direction from within, but through pressure from without. The thoughtless were content to allow the changes to proceed, lead where they would, but the wise were anxious. They began to ask, to use Mrs. Richards' own words: "What are the essentials which must be retained in a house if it is to be the home? What work may be done outside? What standards must be maintained within? How can the schools be made to help? What instruction should go into the curriculum of the lower schools, and what is the duty of the higher educational and professional schools? What forces in the community can be roused to action to secure for the coming race the benefits of material progress?"

But besides great needs, the times presented great opportunities. These are best described, perhaps, in the words of another enthusiastic advocate of organization in the interest of home life, Professor W. O. Atwater, who said, "The science of household economics is in what chemists call a state of super-saturated solution; it needs only the insertion of a needle point to start a crystallization." The needle point was inserted during a social visit which Mrs. Richards made to the Lake Placid Club in September 1898. At that time she was asked to speak to the members of the Club on the domestic service problem, and out of the discussion which followed her address came the determination to hold an annual conference at the Lake Placid Club to consider home problems.

Mrs. Richards' visit to the Club has been described as "social," but it had another purpose. As we know, she seldom traveled merely for her own pleasure or, except in cases of special need, in order to make visits among her relatives and friends. In this case it happened that she had been called upon to advise with Melvil Dewey, who at the time was the Director of the State Library and of Home Education in New York State, with reference to the regents' examinations. The regents had, in 1896, decided to give Household Science a place in the examination tests which the state makes for college entrance, and in outlining the questions Mr. Dewey had turned to Mrs. Richards for assistance. Lake Placid was the summer home of Mr. and Mrs. Dewey, and Mrs. Richards' visit, therefore, was something more than social, since it offered the desired opportunity to talk over educational reforms with Mr. and Mrs. Dewey; it was a chance to push forward the battle line.

Those who loved Mrs. Richards, and they were many, like to think that this crowning labor of hers—the organized home economics movement—had its beginning in a place of marvelous natural beauty, for during her whole life a Puritan sense of duty and a Spartan self-control had kept her in study, in office, and in laboratory when a passion for natural beauty would have led her into the open country. The Lake Placid Club lies on the shore of a quiet lake, which mirrors the mountains and the trees by which it is surrounded. In this beautiful spot in the heart of the Adirondacks, Mr. and Mrs. Dewey had made a home for themselves, reproducing the comforts of their city life and all that contributes to efficiency, and leaving behind all that encumbers and impedes. The Club buildings, of which their home was one, as they increased in number under their wise direction (for Mr. and Mrs. Dewey for some years devoted their time to the affairs of the Lake Placid Club), so found their places in the landscape as to enhance rather than to destroy its beauty. The physical features of the Club were therefore, because of their convenience and beauty, a constant object lesson in the art of right living.

On September 19, 1899, somewhat more than a year after Mrs. Richards' first visit to the Club, the first Lake Placid Conference on Home Economics was held in a room over the boathouse, which may be described as a fresh-air library. To call it a "library" conveys the idea that it was full of books and periodicals conveniently arranged for use, which is correct, but it gives no suggestion of the splendour of its outlook over the water to the mountains, or of the bracing quality of its air. It was a fit place for the organization into a working group of those who were seeking to learn from Nature through Science how to live.

The charter members who met on those beautiful September days of the first Conference were later described by Mrs. Richards: "Six were teachers, lecturers, and authors (two being pioneers in the means of better living and good food—one with much practical experience as well; one wise in rural needs, and two in close contact with school work); there was one with a large heart for the welfare of the race and eager to contribute, one with faith in science as a cure-all, one wise with the wisdom of the future, full of hope and zeal for her sex and its future; one an optimist, with zeal and a belief that to know the right thing was to do it, and one who represented the intelligent housekeeper's side."

Of those who were described by Mrs. Richards as "teachers, lecturers, and authors," there were: Maria Parloa, who was remarkable in this that while she might have argued from her phenomenal success as a teacher of cooking that the informal training which she had received was sufficient, always insisted that those who were to follow in her footsteps must have a scientific basis for their work;

Maria Daniell, pioneer in institutional management and enthusiast for the development of the work to which she had self-forgetfully and courageously given her life; and the one "wise in the wisdom of the future and full of zeal for her sex," Emily Huntington, widely known as the originator of the Kitchen Garden method of teaching housekeeping to children; Anna Barrows, who was "wise in rural needs" because of her successful connection with Grange and Farmers' Institute work; Mrs. Alice Peloubet Norton, then supervisor of Domestic Science in the public schools of Brookline, Massachusetts, but soon to be chosen head of the department of Household Science in the School of Education connected with the University of Chicago; and Louisa A. Nicholass, of the State Normal School, Framingham, Massachusetts, who had organized one of the first normal courses in household arts. The one representing the intelligent housekeeper's side was Mrs. William G. Shailer, president of the New York Household Economic Association, a state branch of a society which shortly afterwards became incorporated in the Household Economics committee of the General Federation of Women's Clubs; and the one described as "having a large heart for the welfare of her race," Mrs. William V. Kellen, of Boston, who had made the School Lunch project possible. The person with "faith in science as a cure-all" was, of course, Mrs. Richards, while Mrs. Dewey was the optimist with "zeal and a belief that to know the right was to do it."

This Conference, which had opened so auspiciously as far as place and membership were concerned, continued for ten years a semi-private organization, with attendance by invitation of the Lake Placid Club, through either Mrs. Dewey or Mrs. Richards. The meetings were always held before the first of July or after the fifteenth of September, when the Club was not likely to be crowded. Through the generosity of Mr. and Mrs. Dewey, speakers and members of committees were entertained. Others were given special rates at the club, without which it would often have been difficult for them to meet the expense of a long journey to the mountains.

The record of the work of the Lake Placid Conference
of Home Economics has been preserved in annual reports
which are a valuable contribution to the literature of the
subject. The story has been twice told in brief; first, in an
address given by Mrs. Richards on the occasion of the tenth
meeting, when preparations were being made for the formation of a national organization; and second, in a carefully
formulated letter of appreciation from the Conference to its
leader. The first is valuable because it gives Mrs. Richards'
own point of view and her own estimate of the value of the
proceedings of the Conference, though it leaves her connection with the work to the imagination of the reader. The
second gives the members' own estimate of the usefulness of
her connection with the organization.

After outlining in her report the conditions which led to
the movement, Mrs. Richards goes into details of the work,
telling first how the Conference set about securing for its
subject a place in library classification which would provide
for development along right lines. In the Dewey Decimal
Classification they had found it entered as one of the useful
arts, but, as Mrs. Richards said, that put it under "Produc-
tion," and the home was no longer an important industrial
center, while it had great responsibilities in connection with
the use of wealth. The Conference therefore insisted that
Home Economics should be classified under "The economics
of consumption." This may seem a little matter, but in that
experimental period it meant very much to give readers and
students a suggestion that Home Economics involves vital
matters connected with social economy as well as the arts
of cooking and sewing.

But much more important was the way in which the
subject of Home Economics was being presented in the
schools. Concerning this, Mrs. Richards said, in a report
referring to conditions in the year 1898:

"Ten years ago domestic science meant to most people
lessons in cooking and sewing given to classes of the poorer
children supported by charitable people, in order to enable
them to teach their parents to make a few pennies go as far
as a dollar spent in the shops. To do this, common American
foods were cooked in American ways, regardless of the

nationality of the children, and usually failed to please the inherited foreign tastes. But complacent philanthropists felt happy in having offered bread to the starving, as they were pictured to be, and pretty bad bread it often was, judged by European standards . . .

"So also the tradition of the valuelessness of a woman's time kept the plain sewing to the front, and classes were taught seams and ruffles and cheap ornamentation in the false assumption that it was economy. As late as the St. Louis Exposition, in 1903, the work of the public schools of this country was almost without exception bad from an ethical point of view, showing waste of time and material and the inculcation of bad taste. The work of the American public schools must have an ethical quality if it is to give us good citizens.

"Almost all the early work in sewing as well as cooking done in the country was wrong, and a plea for a fuller acknowledgment of the economic and ethical was made in the name adopted by the Lake Placid Conference after much thought and a full discussion—home economics: *home* meaning the place for the shelter and nurture of children or for the development of self-sacrificing qualities and of strength to meet the world; *economics* meaning the management of this home on economic lines as to time and energy as well as to money. Lake Placid stood from the first for a study of these economic and ethical problems, let them lead where they would. And they have certainly led very far from the earlier ideals of domestic economy. Real progress is often retarded by trying to make the new fit into the old scheme of things. It has been the endeavor of the program committee to secure speakers and writers with a penetrating vision of the future as foreshadowed by the tendencies to be felt if not seen. Just as the dark end of the spectrum so long disregarded has proved to be of the greatest importance in cosmic interpretation, so the obscure indication of social movements is leading us to clearer conceptions of the goal whither society is tending; and right in the conditions of home life is found the strongest indicator.

"Such topics as the following are found in the programs of these early years: training of teachers of domestic science;

courses of study for grade schools as well as colleges and universities; state, agricultural, evening, and vacation schools; extension teaching; rural school work; home economics in women's clubs with syllabuses to aid such study; manual training in education for citizenship. All these lead toward higher education in better living, the new science of Euthenics, as an essential preliminary to the study of the better race, a study to which Mr. Francis Galton has given the name Eugenics. From the very first special emphasis was laid on the educational possibilities of the work.

"Domestic science at farmers' institutes, simplified methods of housekeeping, standards of living in the conduct of the home and in relation to sanitary science, household industrial problems, labor saving appliances, cost of living, standards of wages and the ever irritating question of tips and fees, have all been discussed.

"Programs have included the food problem in its many phases, from fads and fancies to protein metabolism and mineral matter required by the human body; nutrition, sanitation, hygiene, progress in work for public health represented by the work of the Health Education League and the Committee of One Hundred on National Health, leading to *efficiency* as the keynote of the 20th century.

"Economics in trade and professional schools, home economics in training schools for nurses, the hospital dietitian and the status of institution managers, recent dietetic experiments at Yale University, co-operation with the work of the United States Department of Agriculture at Washington, reports from the American School of Correspondence, even psychic factors affecting home economics and cost of living have been considered.

"The interest of the educator, the schoolman and the woman teacher was no less difficult to arouse than that of the housewife. The school curriculum was sacred to the usual academic subjects.

"Only this past week has seen the fruition of the efforts made by the conference annually to have the subject brought before the National Education Association.

"The teaching section of the Lake Placid Conference, organized in New York in December, 1906, held a full meeting in Chicago, December, 1907, and has collected valuable data for use in further work. It has been the means of uniting the workers of all sections and of making known some of the good work done.

"But after all it is the economy of human mind and force that is most important, and so long as the nurture of these is best accomplished within the four walls of a home, so long will the word Home stand first in our title."

Such was the work of the Lake Placid Conference as Mrs. Richards saw it; her own connection with it is not made evident by her. It was set forth, however, in an address prepared to honor Mrs. Richards, which was presented during the meeting of the Conference in 1905. It was signed by all those who had received the benefits of the meetings, and later it was engrossed, illuminated, bound, and presented to her as a permanent expression of appreciation:

"Every movement for social betterment is made up at its beginning of apparently diversified unrelated forces. Their common ground of agreement, their possible rallying point for combined effort, may be hidden from the ordinary observer, but stand fully revealed to the born leader. To such a one, possessed of imagination and enthusiasm, it is granted to see how this rich variety of experience and suggestion may be used in building up a unity which is yet various, and whose different parts when nourished and grown strong may establish their separate activities. There comes a time in the history of every social and educational movement when the need for thus unifying the work of individuals is so great that without it further progress is difficult, if not impossible."

"Such an organization, Mrs. Richards, was effected by you in the Lake Placid Conference, which held its first meeting in 1899. It was instantly recognized as offering inspiration and practical help to workers in many different fields, to all those, in fact, who were laboring directly or indirectly for the betterment of the home and for good citizenship. It appealed to the student of practical hygiene; to the teacher of sewing and cooking in the public schools; to the kinder-gartner and manual training teacher seeking to establish the relation to brain development of the training of hand and eye; to the educator engaged in outlining the purposes and methods for training; to the adult as housekeeper, as matron of public institutions, as teacher or nurse; to the club worker desirous of finding out the best ways of serving her fellow-citizen; to the thoughtful woman, interested primarily in the well-being of one home, but seeing that many forces must work together for that end. All these students and workers have received help from the Lake Placid Conference in fuller measure than could have been foreseen at its inception. By able committees whose work has extended over several years, it has built up a consistent course of study for elementary, high, collegiate, and technical schools; by the help of another committee, it has obtained through the catalogue system of the American Library Association the proper place for books on Home Economics, thus smoothing the path of the students in this and kindred lines; it has simplified the nomenclature and defined the use of terms formerly employed with different meanings in different schools and localities; it has furnished well-formulated syllabuses for school and club study on Food, Clothing, Shelter, and the Expenditure of the Family Income; it has preserved, in a permanent form in the annual report, discussions by specialists on a large range of topics; it has thrown light on all of these subjects through the co-operation of educators, not only of our own land, but of England, Canada, and Australia; it helped to increase the number of free government bulletins at the disposal of students, by petitioning Congress for additional grants to the Department of Agriculture to be used in nutrition investigations; it has suggested and made possible the establishment of summer schools, evening classes, and courses of lectures in many localities; it has helped in building up the correspondence in Home Economics; it has brought to the knowledge of members the best books on special topics, and has suggested the need and the scope of new ones, such as that valuable series on The Cost of Living, The Cost of Food, and The Cost of Shelter, all of which have been written since the Conference was organized.

"One of the chief functions of the Lake Placid Conference has been to put in touch with each other persons of like interests and pursuits from widely separated parts of the country. This has often resulted in bringing to a given work the very worker who could successfully carry it forward and has made it possible to bring together students of special subjects for the giving of valuable courses of lectures. At these conferences the brave and enterprising West has come to learn of the more experienced East, and the East has in turn learned of a vast and prosperous region where home life and farm life still have the old, close relation which has furnished ideal conditions for character building.

"The dominant note in the deliberations of this Conference, that which has given it its distinctive character, is the ever present sense of the end for which all this educational machinery exists, 'the promotion of healthful, moral, and progressive home and family life, the indispensable basis of national prosperity.' The Conference has repeatedly pointed out that 'no person has a better opportunity to separate convention from good living than the teacher of housekeeping methods.' That there may be 'standards of living,' and that light may be thrown on them by acknowledged principles of economic and social science, and that these standards should be treated from the point of view of their relation to physical and moral health, are doctrines which have taken form in this Conference with clearness and force. It has been recognized that the home cannot adjust itself to the rapidly changing conditions of modern times without help from trained people working through the only medium, the school, hence the importance of placing courses in Home Economics on a sound educational and scientific basis.

"Best of all, this Conference has been characterized by a sunny atmosphere of courage, helpfulness, and enthusiasm. It has been especially full of inspiration to the young teacher. 'For two years,' said one, 'the Conference gave me all the help I had.' 'What I learned that others had done nerved me to the task of starting practical courses in the rural schools of my state,' said another.

"It is impossible to give due credit to all the different factors that have united in producing this whole, making of it an educational influence which it is believed will be a power for good in the land. The name and place of meeting suggests the debt of the Conference to Mr. and Mrs. Melvil

Dewey, who, not only by their generous hospitality, but by their wise counsel and encouragement, have made the Conference possible. But there has been no doubt in the mind of even the most casual observer of the Conference that you, its Chairman, were the inspiring genius and leader of it all. It is you who have drawn around you these workers from far and near and given them quickened thought and a vision of how 'all things work together'; it is you who have ever seen the main issue clear through confusing details and have pointed out not only ideals but the open way to their realization. But we who love and honor you can give no better proof of our feeling than to obey what we know would be your wish, and leave unwritten the volume of your good deeds.

" 'Our chief want in life is someone who shall make us do what we can. There is a sublime attraction in him to whatever virtue is in us.' "

Never was there such a leader as Mrs. Richards. Before she came to a meeting of the Lake Placid Conference she had her plans all fully laid in accordance with her idea of what was due to the busy people whom she was bringing together. She had provided, too, for reports in newspapers and periodicals, and had decided how she herself would use every hour, almost every minute. Arrived on the scene, she was up at daybreak preparing for the day's work. In some way she succeeded in making everyone want to be on hand at the right moment and to fill his or her part in the program creditably, whether it was in speaking, in committee work, or the recording or reporting of proceedings. She could cut off fruitless debate without injuring anyone's feelings, and could bring out all of value that the members had to contribute, and at the same time suppress all that was irrelevant. A certain prosperous business man who was a guest at the Lake Placid Club used often to come to the door of the room where the Conferences were held and stand for a few moments watching and listening intently. The cause of his interest was for a long time a mystery, but finally he was heard to say: "I always like to see that little woman conduct a meeting. It is an education in itself." But he could see only how she was directing those forces which she had in hand at the moment. He little suspected that her generalship extended beyond the time and the place of the Conference, and that the effective ordering of the programs was only one manifestation of her organizing ability.

She always insisted on the subordination of social features to the real work of the Conference. An early morning climb to the top of "Cobble," a hill near the Club, might clear the brain for a day's work, and she would enter into such an expedition with enthusiasm. But upon festivities which took time and energy that ought to go into the work to make it effective, she looked with disapproval.

As a means of "getting things done," the Lake Placid Conference was a working body which might well stand as a model.

Although the Lake Placid Conference retained for ten years the name of the place where it was organized, it held two meetings elsewhere; one in the year 1903 in Boston, where a joint session with the Manual Training Section of the National Education Association was held, and one in 1908 at Chautauqua, New York. It was at this last-named meeting that plans were laid for changing the Conference into a national organization. Mrs. Richards had always had in mind that such a change must come in time, but she believed that it would be most unfortunate if the larger organization came into being before the smaller one had been effectively organized and its work thoroughly systematized. She believed firmly that good work was to be preferred to large size and wide public notice. At the ninth Conference at Lake Placid, in 1907, in reply to a question why a larger organization should not be formed, she replied: "We have started a separate Teachers' Section which will bring together teachers from all over the country and which for this reason is planning to meet at other places than Lake Placid. Let us see what it will accomplish; the national association will come in time when we are ready for it."

Early in the Conference of 1908, with characteristic method, she asked that written suggestions be handed in at a later session as to (1) the most important work for the Conference for the next ten years, and (2) the desirability of organizing into a national body. She had questioned some individuals in advance by correspondence and was apparently herself convinced by the enthusiasm evinced in the Teachers' Section of the advisability of reorganization, but she would proceed only if the members desired and if they could show that they had a large program for the years to come. A preliminary committee on national organization brought together suggestions from various quarters and reported its conclusions that the time had come for a national society with state branches and for the publication of a journal. It recommended that a committee be appointed to report at the meeting of the Teachers' Section which was to be held in Washington in December 1908.

In the fall of 1908, Mrs. Richards published two Bulletins to further the organization of the new association, for which she herself provided the material and took the financial risks. The first contained eight pages, and stated succinctly the purpose of the new organization and asked the cooperation of all who were engaged in trying to solve home and education problems—housekeepers, teachers, physicians, architects, health officers, economists, sanitarians. The Bulletins also contained news notes, queries, bibliographies, and advertisements, the purpose being to indicate the various ways in which a journal published by the new organization might prove useful. The second Bulletin, which was twice as large as the first, opened with the program of the meeting for reorganization to be held in Washington. Thus passed the Lake Placid Conference, but only in name, for its spirit and work were to continue and in a much larger field.

Chapter XIV

THE HOME ECONOMICS MOVEMENT

ON DECEMBER 31, 1908, the American Home Economics Association was organized in the city of Washington, at a meeting held in the auditorium of the McKinley Manual Training School, under the auspices of the recently organized Teachers' Section of the Lake Placid Conference, and Mrs. Richards was chosen as its first president, an office which she continued to hold until the annual meeting in December 1910, when she insisted on retiring and was made honorary president.

Into the work of the Home Economics Association she entered with all her great enthusiasm, believing that though its field was not very exactly outlined, nor very clearly marked off from that of any other applied science, it was sufficiently well defined to warrant bringing together a band of workers into a separate organization. So far as there was a distinct field for the work and a definite body of knowledge, the credit is due to her. On this point Dr. C. F. Langworthy, of the Office of Experiment Stations of the United States Department of Agriculture, says: "To Liebig belongs the credit more than to any one else for bringing together isolated facts and for so adding to them as to produce the new subject of Agricultural Chemistry, which is almost the same as saying Agriculture, as we understand it at the present time. In the same way Mrs. Richards did more than anyone else to bring together a great many known facts and to add a new member, Home Economics, to the group of subjects which a man or a woman may select for serious study or for practical application."

To the details of organization she gave her careful attention. She realized that she had of necessity dominated the older organization, rendering constitution and by-laws of little importance, and that there was little in the way of precedent to guide. In her care for the working machinery of the new

154

association, she seemed to be looking forward to leaving the work, and may have had a premonition of her death which was so soon to come.

The Association developed rapidly after its foundation; within a few years it included many district and state branches, which covered a territory extending from New England to California. These branches as they grew in membership and awakened communities to their local needs divided and subdivided, and thus multiplied in number. Besides the local branches there were sections which brought together special classes of workers—the Teachers' Section, which usually met with the National Education Association, and the Administration Section, chiefly interested in institutional housekeeping, which met at the Lake Placid Club. Signs [in 1912 when this book was first published] pointed to the organization of a Housekeepers' Section.

At the first convention plans were laid for the publication of a journal, and soon afterwards Mrs. Mary Hinman Abel, of Baltimore, was chosen editor. It was decided to publish five times a year, in February, April, June, October, and December. The financial burden of the enterprise, or at least the burden of financial responsibility, fell upon Mrs. Richards, and it was no small weight. Since Home Economics is concerned with the fundamental needs of human life—with food and clothing and shelter—and these needs are at the foundation also of great commercial enterprises, keen after profits, the publication of a journal such as the Association wanted presented some great and unusual problems. Mrs. Richards' wide experience and connections were of greatest value in steering the new publication around the many danger points.

As the organ of a society which brings together widely different groups—teachers in all grades of schools from the kindergarten to the university, housekeepers, lecturers, lunchroom managers, and institutional housekeepers—the *Journal of Home Economics* presented other puzzling problems; what interested one did not interest others; what one needed another did not. At the last executive committee meeting which Mrs. Richards attended, about a month after her retirement from the active presidency, she said that such time in the future as she could give to Home Economics would be spent upon the development of the *Journal*.

To forward this work by a periodical was no new idea with Mrs. Richards. When in 1894 she was approached by an advertising agent who wished to use the name "New England Kitchen" for a magazine that he planned to start, she quickly appreciated this means of reaching more people, but she consented only on condition that she choose the editor. The promoter soon withdrew from the enterprise, and it was managed by a board of editors who took up the work through Mrs. Richards' influence.

The magazine outgrew the narrower title and became the *American Kitchen Magazine*. During the ten years of its publication Mrs. Richards, though never directly responsible, aided it by advice and in securing financial support. The revision of one of her books, "The Chemistry of Cooking and Cleaning," in which S. Maria Elliott collaborated, was published in its pages, and there were few numbers that did not contain some article that she wrote or suggested. She also gave courses of lectures in a Summer School that for several successive years was held by the magazine in its rooms in Boston. This was the first periodical that represented the teacher's point of view in Home Economics, and it exerted an educative and unifying influence that did much to prepare the way for organization.

In 1909 the Association decided to assume direction of the Graduate School of Home Economics, which had existed for several years as an independent organization, but which voted to seek affiliation with the American Home Economics Association. This school offered important opportunities for graduate study in its biennial summer sessions of six weeks' duration. It had its origin in 1902, when Professor Atwater, of the Office of Experiment Stations, opened his laboratories at Wesleyan University, in Middletown, Connecticut, to teachers of Domestic Science, inviting them to study there for four weeks and to get in touch with the government's investigations on nutrition. That same year a call was given for graduates in Agriculture to gather at Ohio State University to do advanced work, and from the two meetings arose the Graduate Schools of Home Economics and Agriculture.

They had their first joint session at the University of Illinois in 1906, their second at Cornell University in 1908, their third at the Iowa State College of Agriculture in 1910. Before the Graduate School of Agriculture the latest investigations in agriculture and kindred fields were reported, one or two distinguished foreign scientists as well as many American investigators being on the faculty each year. In many cases the lectures in this school, those on such subjects as animal and plant physiology, nutrition, dairying methods, and landscape architecture, for example, bore quite as closely upon home as upon farm problems, and the joint sessions for this reason were of great advantage to the Graduate School of Home Economics. Mrs. Richards was actively interested in all the sessions of these schools, and during that of 1908 delivered a course of lectures.

Considering her passionate desire for equality of educational opportunity for men and women, the preference which she often expressed for working with men and women together and not with women alone, and her vigorous protests against special concessions to women, it may seem strange that Mrs. Richards should have interested herself in the Home Economics Association, whose membership consists largely of women, and in the home economics movement, which is often thought to interest women chiefly. It is not a woman's movement, however, but a "home" movement in which men and women alike have been given a part, and the Home Economics Association has many men in its membership. "I think it needs all the wisdom available to attack so great a problem," Mrs. Richards once said, "and I prefer to give my time and influence to work in which men and women are in accord." The fact that men and women are found working together in this Association is due in large measure to Mrs. Richards' influence and to her constant emphasis on the scientific and economic bearings of the subject. Dr. David Kinley, of the University of Illinois, has said: "She had very clear notions of the scope and importance of household economics, not only in the narrower sense in which the term is commonly used, but with reference to the relationship of the subject to general economics and sociology. To her, household economics was a distinct and important phase of the social economy. This seems to me the true view, and to Mrs. Richards more, perhaps, than to any other one person, is due the credit of widening the horizon of the students of her subject, and of enthusing them with a deeper and more tolerant social feeling."

Her position in the matter of woman's work in those fields where it is brought in competition or comparison with men's work was very clearly stated in the course of correspondence which followed an invitation to become a member of the Board of Lady Managers of the World's Fair at Chicago and to exhibit in the Woman's Building.

"I would do anything in my power which you asked of me, but I have racked my brains in vain to find anything which as a woman I have done by myself, which could be shown as woman's work. The only thing I can think of is the little course on mineral lessons which I got out with Miss Crocker for the public schools. You are welcome to copies of my little books and papers on scientific topics, but my work in the main is so interwoven with that of the men here that it is impossible to separate, and it would be an injustice to do so. The work on the water belongs to the State Board of Health and will be shown by them. The 200 young men and 100 young women, my pupils, are my best exhibit and they are not available.

"Massachusetts usually leads and she has left behind her the period of woman's laboratories and woman's exhibitions. Our own Tech has known no sex since 1884 and no profession or occupation is now closed to a perfectly qualified woman. Hence it is appropriate that the space should be left vacant. You might have a large banner, 'Massachusetts points to her women, their works do follow them.'

"Really I see nothing to be shown unless a list of women occupying public and professional positions in 1893 in the State be inscribed on parchment and framed.

Later she wrote even more emphatically:

"From the first I have declined every appointment on the women's branch of the Auxiliary and I do not know how it happens that my name is still on your council. . . . I do not wish to be identified with a body, the very existence of which seems to be out of keeping with the spirit of the times. Twenty years ago I was glad to work on Woman's Boards for the education of women. The time is some years past when it seemed to me wise to work that way. Women have now more rights and duties than they are fitted to perform. They need to measure themselves with men on the same terms and in the same work in order to learn their own needs. Therefore the establishment of a separate woman's branch of our exposition seemed always a mistake to me and one which I preferred not to be connected with in any way. . . ."

She recognized, however, that there are certain forms of work that will always fall to women, and she felt it an injustice that these and the educational problems connected with them do not have the best thought of men as well as of women. Once after pleading before an educational conference of which she was the only woman member for a thorough system of training in home economics, she was confronted by certain old arguments to prove that if women would stay at home and meet their obligations there would be no need of industrial training in the schools. At this time she made one of the most impassioned speeches of her life.

"Industrial training *may* make matters worse. That is why I make this plea, for it may take more and more the interest from home life which, I must reiterate, has been robbed by the removal of *creative* work. You cannot make women contented with cooking and cleaning and *you need not try*. The care of children occupies only five or ten years of the seventy. What are women to do with the rest? All the movement for industrial education is doomed to fail unless you take account of the girls. You cannot put them where their great-grandmothers were, while you take to yourselves the spinning, the weaving, and the soap making. The time was when there was always something to *do* in the home. Now there is only something *to be done*.

"We are not quite idiots, although we have been dumb, because you did not understand our language. We demand a hearing and the help of wise leaders to reorder our lives to the advantage of the country."

Instead, then, of being inconsistent with her ideals, Mrs. Richards' connection with the home economics movement was most consistent, for she believed that because women had clung to antiquated ways of doing housework or of getting it done, and had failed to take hold of their own problems in a masterful way, they were handicapped when they tried to do systematic work outside of the home for which they might have special talents. "The work of home-making in this scientific age must be worked out on engineering principles and with the co-operation of trained men and trained women. The mechanical setting of life is become an important factor, and this new impulse which is showing itself so clearly today for the modified construction and operation of the family home is the final crown or seal of the conquest of the last stronghold of conservatism, the home-keeper. Tomorrow, if not today, the woman who is to be really mistress of her house must be an engineer, so far as to be able to understand the use of machines."

In 1900 she wrote an article for the *Woman's Journal,* in which she said:

"In the strenuous life of a modern community, distractions crowd so closely upon every hand that unless a woman has method in the use of her time, it is frittered away and nothing useful is accomplished. One of the most disheartening things of the day is to see the waste of time and energy in the occupations of nine-tenths of American women. This is the more singular as in manufacturing operations the reverse is so commonly true.

"In searching for a cause it seems at once evident that women, as a whole, have not become imbued with the scientific spirit of the age. They still cling to tradition. They defy natural law, instead of accepting its help in all they wish to do.

"To take one of the most frequent exhibitions of this contempt for law—a woman's behavior in a crowded street-car. Fully three-quarters of the sex do not know how to stand erect in a swaying car, and are not able to keep their balance when the car starts. Yet it is a mere matter of simple laws in relation to bodies in motion and at rest, laws which every school girl should know, and which every school boy does know practically, if not theoretically.

"The first need in woman's education today is a grounding in respect for inexorable law, not only in physics, chemistry and mathematics, but in physiology and in sanitary science, and not least in social-economic science. Too often women have shaken themselves free from the support of surroundings to find that they were ignorant of the rules of the road, and when one has come to grief, she blames conditions instead of realizing her own stupidity.

.   .   .   .

"It is not a profound knowledge of any one or a dozen sciences which women need, so much as an attitude of mind which leads them to a suspension of judgment on new subjects, and to that interest in the present progress of science which causes them to call in the help of the expert, which impels them to ask, 'Can I do better than I am doing?' 'Is there any device which I might use?' 'Is my house right as to its sanitary arrangement?' 'Is my food the best possible?' 'Have I chosen the right colors and the best materials for clothing?' 'Am I making the best use of my time?' "

Her hope for the Home Economics Association in relation to housekeeping she expressed in a few words just after its organization. Having attended all the business meetings of the first convention, she was obliged to be absent from the banquet, but she did not forget her co-workers, and during the festivities a telegram came from her which read: "Happy New Year to the new society! May it celebrate its fiftieth anniversary by the establishment of a new species of housewife."

She believed in the family home with a roof of its own and a plat of ground of its own so firmly that she considered its importance beyond argument. The only question was how to preserve it, and she never could understand how people could, for the want of a little united effort, let it slip out of their grasp and force family life to seek expression in hotels or apartment houses. But she was far from wanting to retain time-consuming methods of maintaining homes. The methods should be determined by the times, and should be the result of the application of science and the principles of engineering. There was nothing inconsistent about working for such homes and at the same time seeking to have the most advanced educational opportunities and professions opened to women.

It should be remembered also, in connection with the organization of the Home Economics Association, that Mrs. Richards was always on the lookout for opportunities as well as for needs. No matter how great or how widespread a need might be, she thought there was little use in trying to meet it by organized efforts until public opinion had reached a point where an effective campaign could be made. As long as public opinion was forming she was continually teaching, preaching, and sowing seed by casual suggestions, but she refused to waste her time in trying to work through organizations until she felt the time was ripe for them. For this she was often criticized and was thought to lack interest in important public questions, but it was simply her way of working.

Her greatest interest, as we know, was in a subject far wider than home economics, and she was watching continually for an opportunity to work effectively along the broader line. She believed that men as well as women should be so educated as to have an intelligent interest in problems connected with food, ventilation, and home sanitation in general, and that every department of life should receive the benefit of applied science. But if the world was ready to revolutionize girls' education in this direction and not boys', that indicated to her where a given amount of energy could be most effectively expended. In the changed attitude of the public mind toward women's education she saw an opportunity to teach the art of Right Living to part of the people at least. "Never mind the name by which it is designated, it is the result we are after. It is not mere hygiene but the whole round of abundant physical life."

Again the home economics movement offered an opportunity to utilize what she once called "that considerable body of useful knowledge now lying on shelves." The *sanitary research worker* in laboratory and field has gone nearly to the limit of his value. He will soon be smothered in his own work if no one takes it. Meanwhile, children die by the thousands; contagious diseases take toll of

hundreds; back alleys remain foul and the streets are unswept; schoolhouses are unwashed, and danger lurks in the
drinking cups and about the towels. Dust is stirred up each
morning with the feather duster, to greet the warm moist
noses and throats of the children. To the watchful expert it
seems like the old cities dancing and making merry on the
eve of a volcanic outbreak. . . . There is ready at hand a
field for the Home Economics teacher."

It is only fair to say of the organization of the Home
Economics Association, that part of the "inconvenience of
ignorance" with which it was destined "to do away" was
the inconvenience to Mrs. Richards of other people's ignorance. From the very first suggestion of introducing Manual
Training and Domestic Science into the schools she had
kept herself informed by study and travel about what the
world was doing. She had herself experimented in teaching
science to children, and had worked with the pioneers in
almost every new educational movement in Boston. She
had, therefore, a fund of information and experience upon
which others were glad to draw, and there poured in upon
her from all parts of the world inquiries as to this kind of
instruction. School authorities wrote asking about the
advisability of modifying the courses in the schools so as
to include Domestic Science and Manual Training; school
superintendents requested her to recommend teachers;
teachers sought positions through her and asked her advice
about advanced work in order to improve their own qualifica-
tions; mothers asked where they should send their daughters
for normal training in household arts; housekeepers asked
her advice about safe economical methods in housework, and
women's clubs asked help in the matter of programs,
speakers, and preparation of papers. She was fairly over-
whelmed with correspondence on all these subjects. No
wonder that she thought the time had come for turning
some of this work over to an organized body of workers, for
teachers to band together and study their own problems, and
for educators to consider in conference the possibilities of the
work.

It may seem strange to some that Mrs. Richards became
a leader in home economics work when her own experience

in teaching had been in a different line. But if all her teaching, informal as well as formal, is taken into consideration, a large portion of it, it is safe to say, was of the kind later given in advanced schools of home economics. This can be said of her teaching in the Woman's Laboratory and also of the lectures that she gave in connection with the Normal School of Household Arts. Just before the organization of the Lake Placid Conference in 1899, she had had a part in organizing the School of Housekeeping in Boston, which was connected with the Women's Educational and Industrial Union. This school, to be sure, as originally planned, was more particularly for the training of household employees, and for two years most of the work was in this line and in the line of lectures for employers of household labor. But the demand on the part of employees and that on the part of the older housekeepers was not great, while at the same time there was a growing demand for training on the part of prospective housekeepers, young women just out of college or high school, and a systematic course was laid out for them. With the beginning of this course Mrs. Richards' interest was thoroughly enlisted, and she became chief adviser in the development of the school and used all her wide influence to interest other people. During the last three years of its existence, from 1899 to 1902, she gave courses of lectures on the Chemistry of Food and helped to outline the related laboratory courses. This School of Housekeeping was in 1902 transferred by the Women's Educational and Industrial Union to Simmons College, and became the basis of the Department of Home Economics in that institution.

A large part, too, of the illustrative material which was used by the first teachers of Home Economics was prepared by Mrs. Richards. In 1886 she employed Charles R. Allen, of the Massachusetts State Board of Education, and Dr. A. H. Gill, of the Massachusetts Institute of Technology, to make after her design charts to show graphically the chemical composition of food materials, and a series of blocks to show the composition of the human body. She had them make, also, sets of bottles containing the actual amount by weight of water, cellulose, proteids, starch, and other substances in one pound of a given food. A short time afterwards Mrs. Richards gave an address before the American Association for the Advancement of Science which she illustrated by means of this material. The lecture brought her work to the attention of Charles Pratt, who was then planning to open Pratt Institute, and he sent for her to come to Brooklyn and advise him with reference to the work for women. The first Domestic Science Laboratory at Pratt Institute was equipped after her plans.

From all this it will be seen that while Mrs. Richards' work in home economics had been largely advisory and had been performed during what she used to call her "play times," it embraced a certain amount of formal teaching and a large amount of practical work. Her researches, too, in her own special line, sanitary chemistry, had at every point served to show her the need of a more thorough preparation for homemaking and had also given her an understanding of possible modifications in educational methods that would make this training available for all women.

Her preparation for the organization of the home economics movement included not only a knowledge of the subject and of the field where it was destined to be useful, but also a capacity for leadership which had made itself manifest in other lines of activity, and which came into special prominence here only because this work offered an exceptionally promising field for her generalship. She had enthusiasm and the power to inspire it in others. She believed in others and made them believe in themselves and have confidence in their own ability. She rated them by what they could do and not by what they were unable to do. Her knowledge of workers in home economics and related fields was wide and her understanding of their powers and capabilities deep. Many of them she had discovered for herself at times when they were trying to decide upon a life work, had been suddenly thrown upon their own resources, or were trying to regain a place in the world's work after having been set aside by sickness or discouraged by failure. Her capacity for establishing intimate, personal relationships where others would at the best have formed only casual acquaintances was unlimited. An introduction after a lecture or at a reception, with a brief word from a person as to her hopes, her difficulties, her aspirations, was sufficient. Henceforth Mrs. Richards had that person on her mind. She sought news of her progress, thought of her when she was asked to recommend workers, sent her literature or helpful suggestions.

Others had recognized the educational need which home economics was to fill and scattered forces had been set in motion. Mrs. Richards went further. She planned a campaign, and through the force of her own personal influence organized a body of workers and moved them forward a solid front.

Chapter XV

FULLNESS OF LIFE

A PERIOD characterized not so much by new forms of service as by enlarging influence, brought to a close a working life in which increasing power had succeeded in finding enlarging opportunities and increasing fitness to teach an enlarging audience. This larger audience was secured chiefly through lecturing and writing.

During the last fifteen years of her life, Mrs. Richards' literary output was very great. Besides scientific papers and magazine articles and published addresses, she wrote the following books: "The Cost of Living," in 1899; "The Cost of Food," in 1901; "First Lessons in Food and Diet" and "The Art of Right Living," in 1904, and "The Cost of Shelter," in 1905; "Sanitation in Daily Life," in 1907; "The Cost of Cleanness," in 1908; "Industrial Water Analysis," in 1908; "Euthenics," in 1910; and "Conservation by Sanitation," in 1911.

In writing these books she had two distinct purposes. The first was to record successful instances of the application of science to the problems of daily life, and the second was to plead for further application. They embodied a large amount of information gained from extensive reading, practical experience, and travel, and were peculiarly suggestive and stimulating. Their style was vigorous and forceful rather than finished. The chief criticism made upon them was with reference, not to their subject matter, but to their arrangement. The wish was, in fact, often expressed that she would spend more time in revision even at the expense of producing less. Her writing, however, was the result of a deliberate plan on her part. She wanted her influence to go toward keeping people thinking and doing, and with this in view she thought that time spent in polishing was wasted. "Keep thinking," she would often put at the end of a letter, and after reading one of her stimulating books it is easy to see in imagination these two words written at the close. She was willing to accept criticism if she could only render the service which she thought most needed at the given time.

She wrote much also that was embodied in other publications than her own. She made valuable contributions to the reports of the Commission on Country Life, and to the Report on National Vitality prepared by Dr. Irving Fisher for the Committee of One Hundred on Public Health; wrote a section on "Domestic Waste" for the Report of the Massachusetts Commission on Cost of Living; contributed several articles on "The Farm Home a Center of Sanitary and Social Progress," to Dean L. H. Bailey's "Cyclopedia of American Agriculture."

Because of its bearing on the relation of the domestic service problem to the labor movement, the report of the Household Aid Company, of Boston, which she helped to prepare during this period, has special importance.

The Household Aid Company was organized in 1903 for the purpose of providing private families with skilled help by the day or hour, and of "studying at first-hand the problems of household labor." Shortly after it was formed, Mrs. Richards said in an address: "We none of us claim that we have found the right new way, but we are sure that every honest attempt to cut a path will help just so much. Light cannot come at once in so great a revolution, but it will come sooner for the efforts made. This little experiment is started, not to help twenty or forty families to live more fashionably or more economically, not to give work to twenty picked women, but to establish a great principle for future practical use. Its breadth entitles it to come legitimately under an educational head."

"It is misunderstood," she said, "because the public assumes that an attempt is being made to ameliorate present conditions. Disabuse your minds of that. The conditions are beneath us, dragging us under; the sooner we cut the ropes the quicker we shall rise to the surface. This is my own message, true or false. It is my belief that we are done with the domestic service ideas of twenty years since. We must, however, have knowledge and patience to try and try again."

Mrs. Richards had an active part in the enterprise from the beginning, but her most important contribution was its

report, which has frequently been commended for the con-
ciseness and clearness with which it presented, not only
the work of the company, but also the social conditions
which were revealed by the experiment. Others co-operated
with her in preparing it, but if it had not been for her
initiative, the work would have passed unrecorded and its
results would have been largely lost to the world. The
story of the undertaking is a good illustration of what has
been called her "tonic" literary style, and it embodies very
many of the shrewd yet kindly observations on life and
people for which she was famous, and which some one has
said ought to be collected into a "Richards' Philosophy."

The report stated in full the commonly recognized disadvantages of household labor to the worker and the ways
in which they were to be met by the company: Required
residence in the house of her employer is not satisfactory
to a self-respecting girl, therefore a house was to be secured,
furnished, and run for twenty Aids *as their home,* not a mere
lodging place. Hours of work were long and indefinite,
therefore the Aids were to go out for a definite period only.
Lack of congenial companionship and recreation was to be
met by making the home life attractive; and injustice in the
demands for service by mediation on the part of the company.

Certain equally well-recognized disadvantages on the part
of the employer—scarcity of workers, low grade of intelligence and of skill, unreliability, danger of infection when
outside help is brought into the house, and the necessity
for frequent changes—were, according to the report, to be
met by establishing an educational test, by requiring six
weeks of training, by investigations of complaints, by a
sanitarily conducted home, and by the maintenance of a
reserve group of employees.

In August 1903, a house was opened as an office for the
company and a home for the Aids. It was decided to receive
young women only after a probationary period of two weeks,
and to require that they be seventeen years of age and have a
grammar school education or its equivalent. The plan was to
give six weeks' training and have the workers available by
October, when the demand would be most active. Ellen A.
Huntington, a graduate of Pratt Institute and of the House-

hold Science Department of the University of Illinois, was chosen as director.

Financially the plan was a failure, and it was abandoned at the end of two years, when the company had lost five thousand dollars; but in the course of the work many interesting facts were brought out concerning the character of household service demanded "in this free and democratic country": the inability of employers to appreciate good service, and their unwillingness to pay for it; and the peculiar difficulties attending such a solution of the domestic service problem as the company contemplated. These facts were so set forth in the report as to make it invaluable for those who sought light upon this peculiar aspect of the labor problem.

Another undertaking into which Mrs. Richards entered during the later years of her life was the Health-Education League of Boston, which published booklets selling for from two to ten cents apiece and disseminated information about hygiene and sanitation by means of lectures. The story of her connection with this organization is best told in the minutes of the first annual meeting held after her death:

"Whatever success we have won or good we have done is due in large measure to Mrs. Richards' wise counsel, self-sacrificing labors, and splendid enthusiasm. She took an active and leading part in the organization of our Society and was Chairman of our Board of Directors from the start. She was present at almost every meeting of our executive committee for nearly seven years. Of the twenty-one booklets that we have thus far published, she wrote five herself, and made the remainder more valuable by her suggestions. She gave many lectures for us without pay, and on one or two occasions when she was paid, she gave us the whole amount for the extension of the work.

"Beside writing the booklets, it was her custom when lecturing in different parts of the country to distribute hundreds of copies free, after paying for them out of her own purse.

"For a long time she desired to do something more to help the great army of workers in shops and factories, and when she was stricken she was engaged in preparing a booklet on Industrial Hygiene."

During these last years she continued to serve as expert in water analysis, examining the water supply of many large corporations and also those of private estates, and giving advice with reference to new supplies. She was frequently consulted, also, with reference to the food of institutions, and during the last three years of her life, according to her own testimony, she "gave advice on the subject of foods in nearly two hundred institutions and acted as general sanitary adviser to two scores of corporations and schools." During these years, also, she was serving as chairman of the Hygiene Committee of the Boston School and Home Association. She was constantly consulted, too, with reference to school lunches, and particularly with reference to the feeding of anemic children in connection with the campaign against tuberculosis.

During all this time, too, she was making frequent trips through the country, speaking before schools and classes in home economics and giving advice about the development of this branch of instruction.

The longest trips of her later years were to Mexico in 1901 and to Alaska in 1903. On both of these trips she took a portable water laboratory and examined the water supplies of many out-of-the-way places, making studies of future possibilities. The results were published in The Proceedings of the American Institute of Mining Engineers and in *The Technology Quarterly*. Her unfailing interest in all phases of life is shown by her diaries, from which the following notes are taken:

"November 6, 1901. Las Cruces. Tired; not up very early; out to river for water; women washing. Took an hour's drive to the silver mines. Wonderful views all the way, surrounded by mountains red and rugged. Green valley with huge trees, green plain, Costilla, cactus, Turk's-head, huge prickly pears, and many desert flowers, jack rabbits, lizards, goats, burros. Stone shelters way up on the mountain where we got good specimens of minerals. The train disappeared so Miss Hyams and I took a mule train—balky mule—to cathedral and shops."

While in Mexico she attended a bull fight because it was in honor of the American Institute of Mining Engineers, which was in session. She did not care for this form of entertainment, but there were some things which she disliked more, as the following entries in her diary show:

"November 6, 1901. Went to bull fight because it was in our honor. There were four bulls, two of which were killed. Horrid!"

"November 8, 1901. Torreon. Old town, so squalid, vile odors, rags, beggars. Beyond description. Narrow, steep, dirty streets. Worn foot stones, five centuries old. A nightmare, *worse than the bull fight."*

It was during these last years that she developed an idea of instructive inspection in connection with sanitary projects. When one of the Boston papers asked her to contribute to a symposium upon what might be done with Boston's share of the money which the Government was proposing to spend on battleships, she outlined a plan for the disposal of waste which involved appropriations for crematory, modern forms of containers and wagons, and also for a full corps of inspectors whose duties should be those of the educator as well as those of the policeman.

One project that Mrs. Richards had in mind at the time of her death was the publication of the Louisa M. Alcott Club Leaflets, which should treat of subjects connected with sanitation and enlightened housekeeping methods in the simple way in which the Rumford Kitchen Leaflets had presented the matter of food. The Louisa M. Alcott Club owed its existence to Mrs. Richards' habit of meditation in the early morning hours. Ideas came which she used to call her "visions," and many of these she hastily jotted down, to be put into being later. A word to Isabel Hyams, in regard to adapting the principles and practices of Domestic Science to the child's intellectual growth and his physical development, led to the establishment of graded courses with equipment for children ranging in age from four to fifteen years. This work has served as a model for other settlements and schools in many cities, and an exhibit sent to the Fifth International Congress on Tuberculosis in 1905, entitled, "Laws of

Hygiene Taught through Domestic Science and Nature Study to children from four to sixteen years old (as a means of prevention of tuberculosis)," was awarded a special silver medal and diploma.

Toward the last, honors came thick and fast, or shall we say that she had throughout a long life of faithful service honored herself, and, as she neared the end, others made public recognition of these honors.

In 1907, she was made honorary life member of the Association of Collegiate Alumnæ, at its annual meeting in Denver.

In October 1910, when Dr. Marion L. Burton was installed as president of Smith College, honorary degrees were conferred upon nine American women. Of these, seven received the degree of Doctor of Humanities; and two, Florence R. Sabin of Johns Hopkins and Mrs. Richards, received the degree of Doctor of Science. The degree was conferred upon Mrs. Richards in the following words:

"Ellen Henrietta Richards, Bachelor and Master of Arts of Vassar College, Bachelor of Science of the Massachusetts Institute of Technology, and there for over a quarter of a century instructor in Sanitary Chemistry. By investigations into the explosive properties of oils and in the analysis of water, and by expert knowledge relating to air, food, water, sanitation, and the cost of food and shelter, set forth in numerous publications and addresses, she has largely contributed to promote in the community the serviceable arts of safe, healthful, and economic living."

On January 7, 1911, the Association of the Women of the Massachusetts Institute of Technology gave a luncheon in Mrs. Richards' honor, and presented her with a purse of one thousand dollars for research work. For this occasion a booklet was published containing a picture of Mrs. Richards in her academic costume, and a large number of pithy sayings collected from her writings.

A growing pallor and shortness of breath, which friends afterwards realized were signs of the approaching end, were the only indications of increasing physical weakness. The three long flights of stairs leading to her office in the Institute of Technology seemed for the first time to tax her strength. Her associates begged her to use the elevator, which, though specially intended for carrying laboratory supplies, was often used to save the strength of those much younger than she. But she refused all such assistance, and went bravely forward on her accustomed way, relaxing in no degree her stern discipline of self.

During August 1910, seven months before her death, there was sharp attack of sickness one night when Professor Richards was out of town, and there was no one in the house to realize the seriousness of the indications. She was at work the following day, giving no sign of what had happened except in a brief note pinned to the wall of her office giving the name of the physician who was to be called in case of sudden sickness.

At the St. Louis Convention of the Home Economics Association, held in December, she was her most active and forceful self, though looking worn. When the convention was over, instead of resting as many younger members did, she looked about her for a theater companion. The following day she made a trip of inspection to the settling tanks along the Mississippi River, and then sped on her way to Boston. On the train she had no thought of resting, for there were those who had been absent from the meeting and must be told about its transactions for friendship's sake.

About the middle of January 1911, she went to New York to deliver an address before the Home Economics Association of Greater New York at its annual luncheon. She chose as the title, "The Conservation of Human Energy," and spoke with her usual vigor, urging again the message which her whole life had carried: "Subject the material world to the higher ends by understanding it in all its relations to daily life and action."

At the time of this visit to New York, she called an executive committee meeting of the American Home Economics Association, and she seemed to take special pains to make it satisfactory so far as work was concerned and to make it unusually gay and cheerful in social intercourse, as if she knew it might be the last and wished the memory of it to be pleasant.

About February 1 she began the preparation of an important paper on "The Elevation of Applied Science to the Rank of the Learned Professions" for the semi-centennial celebration of the granting of the charter to the Institute of Technology. This paper was finished just before her death and published in full in one of the daily papers of Boston on the day of her funeral.

On Friday night, March 17, she lectured at the Universalist church in Haverhill. As the church was but a stone's throw from the house where she was being entertained, it was not thought necessary to order a carriage. On the way to the lecture she was seized with a violent spasm of pain, and was obliged to rest for some time on the road before she was able to go on; but when it was over she insisted on carrying out her part of the program, and lectured as if in perfect physical health.

The following Sunday she gave an address in Ford Hall, Boston, in a course of lectures conducted by the Baptist Social Union, selecting as the subject, "Is the Increased Cost of Living a Sign of Social Advance?" In the address she showed that the high cost of living was due to a growing love of pleasurable sensations and to a habit of speeding up life all along the line, and urged that unless there is a high and noble purpose behind it all, it marks no advance. The audiences at these lectures had a character of their own, being composed largely of those who were wedded firmly to one plan or another of social reform, and were ready to defend their creeds with vigor. While the lecturer was speaking there was a sense of repressed activity, and at the close a volley of questions. Safety-valves we have learned to call such meetings, and have grown accustomed to recognize their value for this purpose. Mrs. Richards was in no physical condition to meet the interrogations which continued for nearly an hour, but her mind was as alert as ever, for her answers came prompt and to the point. This was her last public address.

The following day she was in her laboratory and again on Tuesday, but for the last time. Wednesday and Thursday she was at home, but as she had no definite engagements, it was not necessary to explain to Professor Richards why she did not leave the house. Always mindful of him, and wishing him to have his thoughts free for his work, she concealed from him the fact that she was suffering. On Thursday night, for the first time, he learned that something was wrong when she took a little bell from the mantelshelf in the dining room, saying that she might need him during the night. During the night the call came. A physician was summoned and pronounced the trouble angina pectoris. There followed a week's struggle, during which hope alternated with fear among those who watched with her, and during which her thought was constantly for others. Wednesday morning she seemed to have gained strength, and summoning her secretaries, one at a time, she gave them directions about her work. One she asked to go down town and buy a wicker couch on which she could be carried into her study, there to direct the work of her assistants. Thursday morning she seemed even stronger, but during the day began to sink, and at twenty-five minutes after nine on the evening of March 30, 1911, she died.

On Sunday there was a service for the family at her home, followed by a public service at Trinity Church, where the religious exercises of the Institute of Technology are held. Beautiful Trinity! And never more beautiful than that day when the chancel overflowed with the flowers she loved. At the close of the service the casket was rolled to the west door of the church, and those who had gathered to do her honor saw her last bathed in the glory of the setting sun.

The final service was at the Crematory in Forest Hills Cemetery, and the burial was in the Richards' family cemetery in Gardiner, Maine.

Dead at sixty-eight? No, say rather alive, and abundantly alive, for sixty-eight years, and into that brief span pressing the labors of a century.

Chapter XVI

STILL LEADING ON

IN A WORLD and in an age in which there is a temptation to grasp and to acquire material things, to demand the service of others for one's own selfish advantage, and to claim honor and credit, Mrs. Richards succeeded in living a life in which the current was all the other way. She was the center of a great outpouring. She demanded no service of others, but gave it unstintingly herself; she sought knowledge only that she might give it back to the world in helpfulness; and in spite of the fact that she had earned a substantial income for many years, she died with no money except that which had been given her a few weeks before for research work, and which she had not had time to use.

For the peculiarly outgoing quality of her life, we must thank those unseen powers which determine what our inner impulses shall be; but for the abundance of her service and for its fine adjustment to the needs of her times, we must look to her own splendid determination to set no limit or bound to her labors and to her patient, unremitting efforts to multiply the talents which she had received.

She once said, in speaking of her life, that she had tried to show what an average American woman could accomplish. As to whether or not she was an average person, with the average opportunities of a woman of her period, opinions will differ. She certainly was below the average in the physical vigor with which she was endowed by nature, and such beauty as she had seemed rather the outward conformation to the demands of a strong, sweet spirit than a mere matter of form and color.

Since she had no great endowment of strength, it would not have been strange if her great public labors had been at the expense of attention to those little matters which make life sweet and gracious, but in some way she found time for

> " . . . the whole sweet round
> Of littles which great life compound."

From the stories of her "deeds of week-day kindness" which poured in after her death, volumes might be written. The daughter of an old friend wrote that she had told Mrs. Richards casually in June that she was to enter Vassar College in September, and had not seen her again nor had any communication with her before college opened. Then she found on every hand that welcome had been prepared for her through Mrs. Richards' thoughtfulness. A distant cousin, whom Mrs. Richards had not seen since she was a child, came from the West to study art in New York. Mrs. Richards gave her letters of introduction, and, as the cousin discovered years afterwards, sent money to several friends to be spent in providing the stranger with amusements and diversion during the first weeks of absence from home. A teacher known to Mrs. Richards only as hundreds of others are, moved to Jamaica Plain, expecting to make her presence known after she had become settled, but early the next morning Mrs. Richards was at her doorstep, a pot of hyacinths in her hand, and a welcome to Jamaica Plain on her lips.

She had a way of remembering not only her friends, but her friends' friends, even though they were quite unknown to her personally, and particularly if they were old, sick, or in trouble. It was for this friendliness once-removed that her friends hold her in tenderest affection.

The birthdays of her friends were never forgotten. "True to the day and hour, the greeting from you comes to my hand," one friend expressed it. Nor was the welcome for the coming baby ever forgotten, even in her busiest moments: "It was more than kind of you, in the midst of all the preparations for your journey, to think of me and the little one that is coming. I could not have been more surprised and pleased than when I received your letter and the package (a little lace cap) that accompanied it."

Books and magazines she showered abroad as liberally as she did flowers. Many a year her orders to her publishers for books that she gave away nearly balanced her royalties. She always remembered the libraries in the little towns where she had lived in girlhood, or with which she had special connections. A request from a woman's club in Panama for information about books brought not information alone, but a boxful of books themselves. She had a plan for all the periodicals for which she subscribed. After they had been read by her they were sent to friend, reading room, or club.

In spite of her businesslike attitude toward life, she was sentimental with reference to anniversaries. Two intimate Jamaica Plain friends had birthdays that fell, one near Professor Richards' birthday and the other near her own, and with the two yearly celebrations of the four birthdays nothing was ever allowed to interfere. These celebrations frequently took the form of all-day excursions to the seashore or to the woods, sometimes on foot and sometimes by electric car. "Eventless is your life? Then it is your fault. If you have a good back and twenty cents to spend, you can make a panorama of events pass before you which, like the biograph, will illumine hundreds of otherwise dreary hours."

Her beauty love, which was part of her rich, full life, went out most spontaneously to flowers. She was interested in works of art, but chiefly because she believed that such an interest had a place in a well-ordered life, and she wished to be able to sympathize with it in others. She could work herself up to it, but it never mastered her. With flowers, however, it was different. She raised tulips, hyacinths, and daffodils in profusion in her house every winter, tending them while they put forth leaf and bud, and when they had reached the glory of full bloom, she sent them broadcast among her friends. Part of the ceremony of making Professor Richards comfortable for a long period of work at his desk was to place the best of her flowering plants near by for him to see when he looked up from his books. She understood the needs of plants as she did those of people, and she fed and watered and tended them intelligently, taking no chances. Her reward was the perfection of their beauty.

She loved animals too, horses in particular. But she had not time to give a horse the needed exercise, and for this reason she seldom was able to have one of her own. Kittens came next in her affection, but they were not in favor with those who did her housework, so she finally settled upon parrots. Diaz had a short existence, but Carmen was a familiar household figure for many years, tenderly and intelligently cared for.

She knew the secrets of healing. One summer, when she was taking a carriage trip with a friend in Vermont, she stopped at a farmhouse to inquire the way, and found that a son in the family had just sprained his ankle. In the absence of a physician she gave the necessary first-aid. A few days later her companion, traveling that way, inquired how the young man was doing. The reply was, "Very well, thanks to your friend, the trained nurse."

Though she was keenly interested in professional life for women, she was equally anxious that they should have happy homes. When a young woman who owed her professional training largely to Mrs. Richards' interest and generosity tremblingly told her that she was going to be married very soon, Mrs. Richards said: "I am glad of it. I know him and he is too nice a boy to keep waiting."

She saw no reason, however, why women should lose their individuality in marriage. In writing about marriage as it is portrayed in modern fiction, she said:

"This age is one which is dealing with personal questions concerning spheres, rights, and duties, and anything which will warn from the rocks and quicksands is to be welcomed. The great majority of marriages are getting to be unhappy. The artificial life of our villages, with the struggles for positions as represented by clothes and service, is ruining many a home. I see so much of it in real life that I am glad if any picture can be drawn which will help some to see whither they are tending before it is too late.

"I believe this class of fiction is more wholesome than that which deals with lovers' trysts and escapes from cruel parents only to live happy ever after, marriage being the sum and substance of woman's ambition, and the end of her life. It is becoming recognized that woman has a personality that is not in her husband's control, that the mere fact of marrying him does not make her his devoted slave."

To the quickness of her perceptions and other mental processes may be attributed not only the speed with which she worked, but also the large variety of interests which she was able to keep up. Among her papers were found rough notes she had made upon a slight earthquake shock that had been felt in Jamaica Plain. These notes had been copied and

sent to an authority upon siesmic disturbances, to serve as
far as one person's observations could to determine the
characteristics of the phenomenon. Sitting alone in her
library, she had passed calmly through this experience, and
at the close was able to report which pictures had swung out
from the wall and which had suffered most disturbance.

From the time when she had kept the records at Vassar,
she was interested in forecasting the weather. She always
had a full set of weather maps on hand and followed the pre-
dictions. Occasionally she would think that the prophecy
was wrong, and bringing out the diagrams for half a dozen
days back she would demonstrate her belief; and it is said that
when she and the official forecaster differed, she was quite
as likely to be right as he.

As a result of her many interests, conversation with her
was an invigorating mental gymnastic, and the reaction was
usually a violent effort to bring one's self up to date. Her
sister-in-law, Mrs. Laura E. Richards, gave her the name of
"Ellencyclopedia." In the course of a short conversation she
would refer to this great engineering venture, that man out
West who had made such an interesting discovery, or that
woman in New York who was carrying on such an important
experiment. Those who talked with her usually left her
presence determined to "catch up." Her letters, which had
an exhilarating quality about them and always carried with
them an impression of abiding loyalty, were best described
by the friend who wrote to her, "Your letters are like a breath
of the ocean and a glimpse of the everlasting hills."

Even after due allowance has been made for her quickness,
there is a temptation to say that the way in which she managed to do so many little as well as so many great things
cannot be explained, but it is wiser to admit that it can be
explained in part. She had no more hours in a day or days
in a year than other people, and the fact that she apparently had more at her disposal was the result of thought and
planning. "I wish I were triplets," she once said, and being
unable to carry out this wish, she did the next best thing—
tried to treble the amount of her available energy and time.
She was up and had breakfasted and taken a walk or a
bicycle ride around Jamaica Pond before most people were

out of their beds. She used to claim, half in fun, a peculiarly life-giving quality in air upon which the sun was shining. "The elixir of life is said to be most abundant in connection with the oxygen of air in motion on which the sun is shining."

She saved time, too, by her quick decisions. When, for example, she received a letter, she almost invariably knew by the time she had read it once what she was going to do with it, or what action it called for, and she never handled it again. She made a hieroglyphic on the envelope, which indicated to her the character of the answer to be given and the disposition of the letter. Her handwriting, too, was labor-saving. It was not beautiful and many of the words were only half-formed. The saving came in leaving off the obvious. If the only way in which a word could possibly end and make sense in a given connection was in "ing" or "en," she saw no use of forming these endings. If "wh" could mean only "what" and not "who" nor "whose" in a given place, it served as well as the full word. And her small drawings introduced here and there in her letters often saved many sentences. For example, in one letter, after she had said of two organizations which she was supporting, but not very enthusiastically, "They are plodding on successfully, but without any great object," she made a line of dots which moved bravely forward for about an inch in a horizontal line, and then suddenly curved upward and backward upon themselves.

Her efficiency was due partly to the fact that she wasted no energy in vain regrets. Her yesterdays she put well behind her, except so far as they might serve for guidance in the future. Impatience came nearer than vain regrets to retarding her progress. She wanted to see things accomplished, and when she was irritable it was usually with some one whom she thought to be dawdling. She understood herself in this respect, and not long before the end she said significantly that real happiness had come to her only when she had learned to put seed into the ground and then wait twenty years for it to spring up.

She regretted the foibles, fears, and inconsistencies which she believed were handicapping women in their work, and sought to free herself from them as far as possible. She often preached against them, too. The absence of pockets she never forgot to mention when she heard women demanding their rights. To a friend who held a professorship in a college she wrote: "What is this I hear? Fainting away like a silly schoolgirl? Fie on you! What is the matter with your cook? Take beef three times a day for a fortnight to tone yourself up, and don't do it again. It is fully as important to keep in physical condition as to have a mental grasp. Nowadays the last card they can trump up against us is that we are not physically equal to what we try to do. The more prominent we are, the more closely they watch us. Just now, too, when so much is in the air against woman's education! Think of the example for the girls! Now I know you are going to be sensible and learn just what you can do and what you cannot."

At another time she said: "One of the greatest faults of the women of the present time is a silly fear of things, and one object of the education of girls should be to give them knowledge of what things are really dangerous."

With her perfect self-mastery she was sometimes considered unsympathetic with human frailties, only, however, by those who did not know her personally, and chiefly because she seldom joined in organized efforts to help the weak. There can be no doubt that she loved power, and had a pleasurable interest in all its manifestations, except those involving cruelty, whether they were of man over matter, of man over the dumb animals, or of man over man. She believed in war, or at least thought that preparation for war involved helpful discipline and had been the means of utilizing many of the facts of science which peace had neglected. Fellowship she seldom preached in words, though unremittingly through her unnumbered acts of kindness. It used to seem almost as if, in spite of the fact that she was giving her all for others, she was afraid of putting her thoughts on the subject of co-operation into words, lest she appear to undervalue the help which she believed the individual could and should give to himself, and the self-control and the sense of individual responsibility which she believed lay at the foundation of all progress and should be the end of all education.

Her democracy was of the perfect kind—not that which overlooks differences, but that which does not see them; her faith, which was simple, she once outlined by saying that she "believed in a guiding spirit and tried to keep her ears open to the whisperings and her eyes clear for the inner light." She had a sense of humor which "oft lit up gray eyes with summer lightnings of the soul," and which carried her serenely through many a difficult situation.

Such was the leader's personality. Such a life does not lose its power and vitality when it passes away from us. One catches here and there glimpses of it at work in the life of the world. In the Naples Aquarium laboratories, American women students for years found place and means for research through her efforts and those of others in the Naples Table Association, and her leadership was emphasized also in the Association's Ellen Richards Research Prize. In more than one of the colleges, instructors who came from her laboratory have taught some branch of science as applied to human welfare; her "Euthenics," the science of the environment controlled for right living, is given increasing academic welcome; her bold prophecies and loyal struggles for better living conditions attained through applications of chemistry, economics, science generally, find fulfillment in new curricula and in increasingly intelligent public opinion. One striking testimonial to her continuing leadership is the Ellen Richards Home Economics Fund formed to continue unbroken the activities of research and of propaganda which she initiated for the advancement of the American home.

We can trace her influence at work in many other ways in schools and colleges and other educational institutions, in scientific and popular societies, and in the more efficient activities of public agencies and private undertakings which she touched. Her life goes on in a thousand forms and in a thousand places, and the most skillful social survey could not reveal them all. To those who knew her and worked with her there remains, moreover, the personal presence of the leader, the counselor, the friend, in the laboratory, at the desk, in the conference room and the convention hall— wherever tasks must now be faced alone which once were faced with her.

In Memoriam

ELLEN H. RICHARDS

A voice is hushed: but ere it failed,
  The listening echoes caught its tone,
And now its message clear and keen
  On every wind of heaven is blown.

A staff is broke: but ere it snapped,
  Those who had leaned on it so long
Had made its steadfast fibre theirs,
  And fare now forward, straight and strong.

A light is quenched: but ere it paled,
  It lit a hundred torches' flame,
That shine across the darkening sky,
  And star with gold one honored name.

April, 1911   LAURA E. RICHARDS

Appendix A

April 4. It is really Spring. The ladies' delights are in bloom and the tulips are up three inches high. The birds are singing in the morning.

April 9. I would like to come in and give you my first flowers for I have had the great privilege of finding the white hepaticas, the first spring flowers found this year. Miss Folsom and I found them in our walk about two miles away from the college. We sent a delicate bouquet to poor old Mr. Mitchell (Maria Mitchell's father) who will never see the spring flowers again. We carried a cluster to Dr. Avery who was much pleased and to Miss Lyman who is sick.... The frogs are peeping, the yellow crocuses are in bloom and the hillsides are becoming quite green.

Easter Sunday. I send you a specimen of the walking fern which we found on Cedar Ridge. [A college mate writes: "There was a little Natural History Club of which she was an active member, and long walks in the neighborhood brought home specimens for its meetings. Often she was one of a group of five or six who, regardless of swamps or stone walls or ditches, made their way straight to some distant hilltop, marked from the college windows as a good place for a mountain view. Oftener still her vigorous, elastic step set the pace for one or two in a walk through the fields and woods and her eyes and ears made note of what was best worth observing."]

Dr. Avery has given me permission to rise in the morning when I wish if I will not disturb the others, so I shall gain some hours these long mornings. [The college mate who was quoted above says: "There were no wasted minutes in her calendar. Out-of-doors there was whole-hearted recreation: in-doors, time well-adjusted to accomplish her ends. The tireless industry that later she made so significant showed itself in many ways. There was an hour for going to the library to look through the Reviews and Magazines and Weeklies, culling out whatever had a bearing on her own studies or recorded progress in other fields. There was knitting to pick up between observations at the telescope or to keep time to the learning of German verbs. The knitting needles were active sometimes even on the long flights of stairs that led to her fifth floor room of the senior year."]

April 26. Miss Folsom and I went to the city yesterday for a little shopping. My hat is a soup dish of white straw, with five leaves of the straw edged with black velvet on the top. It cost $2.25. In town we went up College Hill. The view of the city was very fine from the roof of the building which is used for a summer hotel. Miss Folsom and I are the acknowledged champions of the pedestrian excursions. I was not going down the river to West Point, so only the principle touched me. As long as I am always prompt to my classes, and have my lessons well, and have no intimate friend, and mind my own business, my disobedience of one or two rules will be winked at. I do not trouble myself to stay within the red fence when I see something I want the other side.

May 21. Nothing of general interest has occurred. One of the society chapters had an entertainment. At the German table Miss Kapp proposed a paper, to be called, *Die Schwalbe,* the German for Swallow, with editors and a staff of correspondents. I am to collect items and anecdotes and translate them into German.

Do not worry about me. Miss Lyman has no cause to complain of me. I never fail in my college duty, so I do not have to get excused. The faculty have granted my every wish and there is no chance for trouble. I always study causes and effects wherever I am, so I must criticise sometimes.

May 30. (Abstract of sermon by Rev. Mr. Cox, of Brooklyn.) Thanks for your kind sympathy in my suffering (an ulcerated tooth, reported the week before). It was indeed severe, "but this body must be subject to the mind and the philosopher must learn to control his nerves and not let pain hinder the process of his thought," as Mr. Cox so beautifully said. "Serenity is not natural. It is a virtue. Calmness is a Christian grace."

On Wednesday, by a special favor from various officers of the College from Miss Lyman down, I was offered, without my seeking it, a place with a party going across the river on a botanical expedition. I enjoyed the trip very much. It was the first time I had been in a conveyance of any kind since Christmas.

1869-1870

September 21, 1869. It is so good to get back to studying.

Sabbath morning. A message came that Miss Lyman wished to see me in her parlor at eleven. She had fifteen or twenty of the active christian workers to meet her and consult on religious matters in College and make suggestions. We were there nearly two hours.

October 10. I have helped three different girls out of mathematical difficulties during the week and had to submit to being thanked and kissed. I find my eyrie on the fifth floor is not so secluded a place as I had fancied. [Her room for this year was chosen primarily for its secure quiet, but also for its glorious view, with the sunsets over the long, dark line of the Highlands of the Hudson and the peaks of the Shawangunk. There were not more than half a dozen others who for various reasons had chosen these upper rooms, and as they were a fairly law-abiding set, there was no surveillance by corridor teachers and little interruption from idle visitors.]

October 20. One of the seniors, who is in astronomy comes to me sometimes for a little light and she thinks I am "awful good."

My plants are doing very nicely. The rose is growing fast also the ivy, and several geraniums.

The Synods of New York and New Jersey are in session in the city and are coming out to see us this afternoon. We are to assemble in chapel and show ourselves, literally make our best bow, as the President introduces the Moderator. This body visited the ground six years ago and encouraged Mr. Vassar in his undertaking, and the President felt it a duty to ask them out now.

Later. The Reverends have just arrived. A large open wagon, two omnibuses and many hacks and carriages. I should think the whole two hundred were here. College is put in apple pie order for them to see.

October 24. The visit of the Synod passed off well. One hundred and fifty ministers were packed in a dense black mass on the platform to look at us. Dr. William Adams of New York spoke very well. Said he felt it to be one of the greatest privileges of his life, etc.

I have nothing further to record of the past week, only it has been full of blessing and mercy. I have been well, learned much and able to help others.

November 14. As to a box, I should enjoy it during the Christmas vacation, if it won't cost too much and take too much of your time to prepare it. I suppose I do not need it, for I have all that is necessary here, and am getting quite stout. My body does not need pampering. I should like it only because it came from home.

November 21. We are to have company in two classes tomorrow and are to have extra lessons. Much responsibility is thrown on us for the reputation of the College. Nobody knows how we work here. It is really marvelous. No other institution can show whole classes of such hard workers.

November 28. I went down to the meat cellar yesterday and weighed myself, 123 lbs.

There is an article in the North American on the Civil Service Reform which father ought to read in order to keep posted in political affairs.

December 3. One cannot understand Vassar until they have been here. I speak advisedly when I say there is no such work done in any institution in the country. All professors say so who have been in other places. All students say so. One teacher who has been principal of a young ladies' seminary says the same. All bear testimony they never knew what could be done. Our very play is hard work.

December 5. Miss Mitchell says that I may have two little telescopes here during the vacation and make all the discoveries I please. I am planning much for the two weeks. Prof. Farrar says that butyric acid which is formed in strong butter is one of the worst poisons. It works so slowly that one does not know what is the matter, but it undermines the health surely. Avoid strong butter wherever you are.

December 19. The President preached a Christmas sermon to-day. Everybody talks so much about Christmas. I realize fully that I am not in New England, and though I try to be very liberal, yet dear old Massachusetts is dearer than ever.

The senior who read her essay last night suffered everything almost. She cried over it a great deal, and when she went up on the platform she was white as marble. I expected to see her sink to the floor, although she had a fine essay. Prof. Farrar does not think it right to subject the girls to such a strain and he will not go in to hear them. It is almost martyrdom to some of them, for they will be judged by it, however unjustly. Miss Mitchell will not hear any of her girls read, strong woman that she is.

Miss Mitchell told me yesterday that Prof. Henry of the Smithsonian wished someone to undertake the meteorological record here; that I could do it if I would. Instruments would be furnished me and I can keep them after I leave here and continue the work if I please. I shall undertake this. Mr. Mitchell used to do it as long as he was able.

College has been in a ferment to-day. Some weeks ago the Students' Association requested the Lecture Committee to invite Wendell Phillips to deliver his lecture on the Lost Arts. Dr. Raymond told us this morning that we were refused; that the Committee had one member who would not hear him or let any member of his family hear him, and one who would hear him rather than anybody else. The other three members stood between in their opinions. They thought that a man so identified with extreme views ought not to come here as we were not to be exposed to radical doctrines of any sort. "The sacred trust of fathers and mothers" etc. To-night we held a meeting of the

Philalethean Society and requested the secretary to ask the Faculty to have Wendell Phillips lecture before them and that they might sell tickets, so that no one should come unless sensitive papas and mammas were willing. We are about tired of poky lectures. This year has been better than last but we want the best.

December 29. So far this vacation has more than realized my highest anticipations of profit and enjoyment. Friday evening some ten or twelve of us had a candy pull in Prof. Farrar's kitchen, a fine time which he enjoyed as well as we. Saturday evening we all gathered in the college parlors and the President read to us Dickens' Christmas Carol. It was a great treat and everyone enjoyed it. We then had ice cream and cake and a social time.

I never fully realized how much a New England birth was worth. I am so happy that that was my lot. It is a great deal in these days. I feel it so keenly now when I am away from it among a strange people almost. Dear old New England is the home of all that is good and noble with all her sternness and uncompromising opinions.

1870

January 5. The last day of quiet. I am very sorry. I have enjoyed this so much. I have accomplished a great deal in one way and another.

I shall save in money all that I can, for I want a telescope more than anything else. I am perfectly content with whatever clothes I have. I have enough in my head to balance what is wanting on my back. I am just as happy as if I had a dozen dresses, and have come to the conclusion that a contented spirit is a great boon.

With regard to the essays, we would not mind an ordinary essay, but this is felt to be a test of our class standing and an unfair one at that. It is an unheard of thing, so far as I know, in any college and we feel that it is very different from reading at a literary entertainment.

January 23. I went up to Sunrise Hill with Miss Mitchell's niece yesterday morning. It was like May.

January 31. I am doing nicely in all my studies now and am not fretting over the examinations which occur Thursday and Friday. Much depends on keeping cool and I believe I have that faculty.

February 13. I wish you could have heard the good things I have heard to-day. First Prof. Farrar's Bible lesson, taking up the life of David, then this afternoon and evening, Rev. Mr. Sanders of Ceylon, told us of the Island, the people and the work there. I almost wanted to go to India after hearing his stories.

We are fairly on our way now in all our new studies. My yesterday's work was, physiology at 9, astronomy at 9-45, logic at 10-30, chemistry at 12. I learned my physiology and astronomy for to-day between 11-15 and 12. A class meeting fifteen minutes came after dinner. I studied German what time I could find in the afternoon besides thirty-five minutes with a pupil in Latin, forty-five minutes for elocution, thirty minutes with a classmate in astronomy who did not quite understand the lesson, until 5 o'clock, when I rested forty-five minutes, then dressed my hair and myself for tea. After chapel spent an hour with Miss T. in Latin. At 8 o'clock went to the President to hear him read Boswell's Life of Johnson until 9. Took a bath, read over the logic for to-day and was in bed before the bell struck at 10. Wasn't that a good day's work? There were a dozen other little things, such as my weather record, a visit to the steward's department for a bone, a call on my former parlor-mate, etc.

The world moves, but we seem to move with it. When I studied physiology before (when I was a little girl of seven years old) there were two hundred and eight bones in the body. Now there are two hundred and thirty-eight. I think father would be delighted to see Miss Mitchell lecturing me this morning, because I ignored one one-hundredth of a second in an astronomical calculation. "While you are doing it, you might as well do it to a nicety." That is the only thing she has ever complained of me for.

February 20. I am not fretted with my work after all. My lessons are not hard and they are interesting, and I find some time to read, but it is mostly scientific reading. . . .

We have had no good observing weather of late. When it does come, we shall improve it whether we do anything else or not. There is so much to do that, as usual, I shall do part of everything and content myself with that and not try to outshine the rest. I came here for self-culture and not for honors. My talent does not lie in recitation. "Great executive ability" has been Miss Mitchell's and Prof. Backus' only compliment for me.

February 27. Friday I stayed up until nearly half past eleven. I found some star clusters which I thought Miss Mitchell did not know. She was greatly pleased and said to me, "Do not spend any money on knicknacks until you buy yourself a telescope. You will make valuable discoveries in the course of your life."

We had our Chapter meeting Friday night and the criticism of the last meeting was read. The critic of the evening was the best scholar of the class and I was delighted with her criticism of my essay. She said it was well delivered, showed thought and study. There was no attempt at ornament which caused a little lack of smoothness. It had the three elements of a good essay, thought, information, and urging us to action. Monday was a busy day. I went to five recitations, spent three periods with my pupils, went to see Miss Lyman for the first time this year at her request, that she might give me authority to train the delinquents in all their studies "as if you were their mother." . . .

Miss Lyman said today: "Colleges do not pretend to finish, seminaries only do that. They make nice little flower beds with the seeds all planted in rows and the earth smoothed off handsomely. Colleges spaded up the ground deep down and put in guano, mixed it up thoroughly that whatever is planted there afterward has a luxuriant growth."

Yes, I know I take up too many things, I know that I am careless in many ways, I always was, but I can be careful enough when I think occasion requires it, and I have decided that it is not worth my while to use up strength in going against the grain where it is not necessary in order to accomplish a great end. I find that to be my greatest fault but when I see others who have that virtue and yet are so deficient in what I have in great abundance, I am content to do what I can in my own way. Miss Mitchell appreciates highly in me, what she decidedly lacks, business ability and administrative talent, and a quick, clear insight into things. I came here to train myself, not to make a show, and I am satisfied. I am better off than those who are so anxious about class honors. I shall not feel badly if I get none of them. I have not shown my full strength. I have kept in my corner and worked for myself. . . .

I would like to enjoy the quiet with you a little while, but my life is to be one of active fighting.

March 13. My teaching seems to give great satisfaction for Miss Lyman has called me to her twice this week to consult on poor scholars, and has given me charge of her niece and another young girl who do not like Latin. I enjoy teaching and find that my previous teachers were really superior; that my knowledge of Latin has not gone, only faded by reason of dust, and can be brushed up without difficulty.

Of course the event of the week for me was the essay last night which was a complete success. My voice filled the chapel without effort and they said I seemed to have any amount of breath and power unexpended; that I stood there just as though it had been my business to read essays. I never felt more cool and collected in my life, and my face was not in the least flushed, nor did a nerve quiver. I never have dreaded it, but I got off better than I expected. Miss Mitchell would not come because she would suffer so much, although I assured her I should not. I wore my black silk with lace sleeves and my class pin, without a particle of color about me. Everybody else had worn bows and ribbons.

Miss Mitchell was cautioning one of her girls the other day about looking too long through the telescope, but the girl was obstinate, when Miss Mitchell said, "You do not take so good care of yourself as Miss Swallow does."

I sympathize with father and I wish the women's rights folks would be more sensible. I think the women have a great deal to learn, before they are fit to vote.

March 16. In calculus, Prof. Farrar keeps me in reserve to call upon when the others fail. I ask nothing more, only longer days or quicker memory. There is so much to do.

March 20. Once more, it does not pay well to strain one's mind and spend one's time to be sure of rattling off rules or facts, or a string of words in exact order, when there are so many principles lying in them which are rich in thought and information. *I* didn't take the 200 topics in chemistry and prepare for examination by studying from beginning to end, as one girl did. I didn't fail in the examination, as she did, when a question a little off the track was put, and I wasn't sick a fortnight, as she was. I gave much thought to my plan of life here. It was the result of cool deliberate judgment, and I am satisfied with the fruits. . . .

I don't think I can be called an idle individual about now, five studies, laboratory and observatory practice, and earning $1.50 a day, as much as most girls do who work all day. Tell Father I guess I'll beat him. And the money is not all, I have gained so much courage to find that my knowledge comes back to me and that I am successful in imparting it. The recommendation that will be ready for me, will be valuable some day.

Well, I must hasten to the news items. I've been in the Laboratory some time, helping get ready to make some casts for your mantel shelf, and this week we are to begin to learn photography. Last night was a clear night, for a wonder, and I was out on the stone steps of the Obervatory two and one-half hours, and got pretty tired. There was a beautiful aurora, red streamers and brilliant white ones. The night before, we saw the planet Uranus, through the great telescope, seventeen hundred million miles away.

March 27. I am getting a reputation for knowing all that occurs in the out-door world. Miss Mitchell sends to me if she wants to know what happened in the night, or how the stars looked at a certain time. Dr. Avery told one of the girls on this floor that if she wanted anything in the night, she could call on me, for I was a spook. I was amused, for I had never heard that term. I believe it is the darkey term for ghost or spirit, that wanders about in the night.

Without date. Tuesday night we heard more of the eccentric Sam Johnson. The President requested the girls to bring their knitting work.

April 3. (From one of the latest works on physiology, a lot of rules on cooking and food.)

April 10. Five of us left the College yesterday morning (this was the Easter vacation) for Fishkill, in search of a Graphite Mill which our textbook in mineralogy said was there. That was all we knew. (Follows a full account of the trip).

I was up in the night and found seven new star clusters, and three new nebulæ, which will delight Miss Mitchell.

April 17. I shall wear my white dress to graduate in. I could have nothing prettier. Miss Lyman said that she did not know why we should have *new* dresses, and I can do my share toward creating a different style of dress. A senior has some influence you know, and the professors, especially Prof. Van Ingen, are much opposed to long dresses and finery. It hurts the College. I have lived up to my principles on dress while here and hope that I have done some good.

April 24. I do not see the use of a veil for me. I never wear one over my face and I do not want it because it is the fashion. That is against my principles.

May 1. I shall have to wait until I see you for my raptures over George William Curtis. He made himself doubly dear by asking it as a privilege to do so much from love and not for pay. He spoke of our having an opportunity to show what our needs and capacities were, not in a hot house, but like a tree, symmetrical in all directions. It was the best women's rights speech I ever heard. Suffrage, the ballot or rights, were not mentioned. [A large photograph of Mr. Curtis hung in her bedroom up to the time of her death.]

Wednesday. I hope I can remember Miss Mitchell's story of her experiences at Rome when I get home, how she got into the Observatory of Father Secchi, which no woman had ever entered, and where Mrs. Somerville and Caroline Herschel had vainly tried. How she would not ask the Pope herself, because she would have to kiss his hand, which she thought beneath the dignity of an American, but she got Mr. Cass, the American minister, to get her permission.

Tuesday. As Lizzie Coffin and I went in to Chemistry class to-day, Prof. Farrar said, "Dr. Coffin and Prof. Swallow."

Appendix B

LETTERS FROM JOURNEYS
(Included in Chapter XIII in previous editions)

ST. LOUIS HOTEL, QUEBEC,
August 12, 1872.

Here we are in a pouring rain, quartered in a very elegant apartment going to bed for a sound night's sleep. Yesterday we dined in a log house or what was very near it, unfinished boards at least, used only during haying for the farm hands; the table unpainted, leaves not up, no cloth, old blue ware, a plate of three biscuits large as saucers of the "black bread" variety, a saucer of brown sugar for the tea, milk and "yarb" tea (very likely English Breakfast). We dined at 12. Today we dined at 6, small square tables covered with finest damask, printed bill of fare with six courses, waiters in "full dress," swallow tailed coats. . . . We have had varied experiences since I wrote, mostly very pleasant. Yesterday I had the pleasure of driving all day, one of the finest horses I ever saw, and visiting three copper mines, getting a fine lot of specimens and learning a great deal about the country and mining.

TRURO, NOVA SCOTIA,
June 13, 1875.

We have had a prosperous week and have carried out all our plans. I have been resting and am very nicely and I think Robert is none the worse, although he has the care of the expedition. We have visited the Albert mine, the famous Joggins and the Arcadia Iron mines. I have been the botanist of the party. We are just in time for the early Spring flowers. In St. John the trees were just starting; here they are just blooming. We have not exactly lived in clover, but have not been very badly off yet.

ZURICH, July 16, 1876.

We spent an afternoon and night in Interlaken with Professor Crafts and his wife and there saw sunrise on the Jungfrau. It was the finest thing I ever saw. It was so hard to come away and not go to the mountain when we were within fifteen miles. The Swiss wood carvers live in this village. More than a thousand people work at it here. The life is so sweet and peaceful and so beautiful in its surroundings and simplicity that Robert wished he could live there always. The little Swiss chalets are exceedingly picturesque, and they look so neat and clean. The women and children are bright and smart and they don't waste time in fine parlors and flounces. They can turn hay or carve wood and speak three languages.

COLOGNE, July 22, 1876.

It is so strange to be where everything has been made from earliest time. We cannot realize it, we whose grandfathers conquered the wilderness, what it is to live where the same houses and streets have been just the same for a thousand years and to live on a spot inhabited for more than two thousand years.

. . . .

Nature has done much for our country and man is rivalling nature as was perhaps natural in a country where Nature, as it were, defied man. A new race is springing up to whom the labors of Hercules will not seem impossible. But I must not ramble on this way. I am an enthusiastic Yankee and I am afraid I am of the present age which tears away the veil to see what is behind.

DRESDEN, August 6, 1876.

We are all bewitched with Dresden. The Gallery of Paintings is a revelation to us, the pictures are so *beautiful*. I want so many of them in photographs that Robert is laughing at my extravagance. I have been so good until now, but now I am spending such a lot of money.

LEIPSIG, Monday, August 7.

We arrived here this evening. Walked out and took in the general features of the famous university town and remarked on the *variety of its odors*. [Mrs. Richards had what has been called an "educated nose."]

BRUSSELS, August 13.

At Liége we spent one day in visiting the immense iron and zinc works. Then we came on to Brussels yesterday. There we visited the International Exhibition of Hygiene and Remedial Appliances, and saw surgeon's bandages, hospital cars, health clothing, etc. . . . On our return home we shall go to the Centennial exhibition at Philadelphia. We shall remain about a week I suppose and I want you [her mother] to go with us. I have decided to give you that pleasure instead of the checked silk dress which I intended to bring you.

September 5, 1877.

I expect to get my vacation in going to the Tennessee exhibition as juror on Education in October.

GARDINER, MAINE, 1879.

We have just been to the American Association meeting at Saratoga. I appealed to the chemists there to help in this matter of Household Chemistry. I seem to have got drawn into that track now and must follow it out whether or no. It is an open field but much study will be required in it. I am to prepare a paper, on the ingredients of food liable to adulteration, this winter.

CALUMET, MICHIGAN,
July 8, 1881.

I have the laboratory work about started and have just enough to do to keep me from being lonely. I have a young man to wait on me and I shall find it hard to come back to do my own cleaning up. In fact it is very good fun. The only trouble is that it looks as though I were not going to see Robert but once a week. He went down to the mill at the Lake on Wednesday and is not coming back until Saturday night. However, it is only five miles and the ore cars go up and down several times a day and besides there is telephone communication between the two offices. On the whole things are going as well as can be expected and we have reason to be satisfied. It will be good experience for both of us. I only hope you [her mother] will keep comfortable. . . .

This is Yankee land even if it is so far away.

CALUMET, June 17, 1882.

[To her mother]

I wish you could take one walk through these woods. Such a profusion of wild flowers and such luxuriant growth I never saw before. I have been out nearly every day and my room is full of bottles and tumblers of bloom. I have found some 25 kinds already; most of them are familiar friends but two are new to me.

DENVER, COLORADO,
August 20, 1882.

Here I am enjoying my first glimpse of the West and of the old Rocky Mountains. Miss Cushing (Vassar 1874) and Miss Minns came to Calumet about the first of August, and staid with me two weeks. Then we went to Duluth, thence by the Northern Pacific as far as Fargo. We spent such an interesting day there. We rode through the wheat fields which extend for thirty miles and in one day we gathered 67 new flowers. We came down first for a day in St. Paul, then a day in Omaha, then on here. We enjoyed it all. Miss Minns and I had never seen the plains and we got much excited over the flowers. We start on Monday morning for ten days among these lovely mountains with the Institute of Mining Engineers. We shall see nearly all the nice things. I go directly back to Calumet to finish my work there. [In 1879 Mrs. Richards had been elected a member of the American Institute of Mining Engineers in recognition of her scientific work. She was the only woman ever elected to active membership.]

ON THE TRAIN,
September, 1882.

I have come back from the West with the feeling that our Eastern people make a mistake to go to Europe year after year and never to really visit our Western Country. The enterprise and bold venture of the people and the lofty mountains and deep cañons and vast plains seem to me to be far more interesting than the sleepy ignorant peasant living on black bread with no thoughts or ideas above it, or than the piles of stone already crumbling at the base before the top is finished. When I emigrate from New England I think I shall go West, where there is a little "go" in the air.

LOW MOOR, VIRGINIA,
June 19, 1883.

A good deal has happened in the last twenty-four hours. When I stopped writing we got on to the flat car and were taken down by gravity, coasting the three miles. It was a novel experience for most. Then we started up suddenly to go into a cave just opened in getting limestone where there were iron ore stalactites as well as calcite ones. It was the roughest trip I ever took. I went up a rope some thirty feet almost hand over hand and then stumbled over the uneven ground of the freshly opened cave. I got muddy from head to foot but we got some lovely things and it was a spicy adventure, especially the coming down.

GARDINER, MAINE,
September, 1883.

We are having a few days on the Kennebec at my husband's old home. I dare say I have written to you before from here. It is very lovely although the drought has left the hills brown and is taking the leaves from the trees very fast. Now and then we see some brilliant tree but I fear the colors will not be fine.

Our occupation here is social gayety, strange to say, tea parties and dinner parties, evening after evening, or excursions by water or land. The family has a steam launch carrying some twenty-nine persons which is very convenient for excursions. We all went down to the sea at Booth Bay on Monday. It was a perfect day and we had five little girl cousins to enliven the older people.

BIRMINGHAM, June 12, 1884.

The grand Educational Conference at the Health Exhibition is to be held August 4 to 9 and I must be here then so we shall be off for Norway July 1st. Tuesday June 24 I spent solid at the Health Exhibition.

STEAMER ANGELO, NORTH SEA,
July 5, 1884, 8.30 P.M.

At the present moment the sun is nearing the horizon and sending to us a broad path of orange-red light while the gentle billows all around are tinged with the most beautiful shades. The moon, nearly full, beams upon us the other side. A vessel with curiously shaped sails lights up just astern. We have seen so many vessels today, it seems not at all a desert waste. The craft are all small but very picturesque with their colored sails.

11 P.M., July 14, 1884.

We are just crossing the Arctic Circle. I do not see any special ceremonies going on but I must write up today's journal on the spot. I wish you all could see this landscape. We are making for some high islands which are green nearly to their tops with many houses on the low shores. Directly behind there is a high snow-capped range of very serrated peaks. The quarter moon hangs large and bright a little above the horizon at an angle of about 45° from our course. On the left at about the same angle is a low place in the mountains which glows with the sun just below the horizon. It did not disappear until 10.15. The light over all is indescribably beautiful. Robert will know a little how it is from our beautiful Calumet sunsets.

1 o'clock, July 15.

We are still sitting in the shelter of the prow where we were at 11. The sun is nearly rising and the colors are wonderful. These two hours have been a succession of marvels. We have been passing among the strangest shaped peaks and in sight of high mountains, snow-capped. It is all so strangely beautiful that it must be seen to be at all appreciated.

1.45 P.M.

We are still here. It has been too delightful to leave. The Captain either gulled the people or they misunderstood him for we are now just crossing the Arctic Circle, just as the sun is going to appear behind some high hills which have hid it.

REDRUTH, August 13, 1884.

We reached Truro one hour late last night about 9 o'clock. Found the Red Lion very nice and historic, 1631. This morning we visited the museum and the town, saw a smelting house under repair, had an hour's talk with the people, got a good basketful of specimens and took the 1.30 train for this place, where we shall visit the Mining Institute and some smelting works in operation.

The following letter was written to Mrs. Rogers, widow of the founder of the Institute of Technology, who had shared her husband's pioneer labors and retained after his death a vital interest in the Institute. Mrs. Richards was always at pains to keep her informed about the work, and used often to spend a few restful days at her Newport home, which she once described as "within sound of the breakers, away from all sound of the Newport life."

GRASS VALLEY, CALIFORNIA,
July 3, 1885.

We spent a week in Denver and Boulder and a day in Pueblo where there are three of our graduates. . . .

Our greatest trip was the Grand Cañon of the Colorado river. We did not of course follow Powell on his journey on the river itself, which must be very dangerous, so we did not get the full grandeur of the gorge, but we saw more than we could take in of the mighty cliffs seamed with these rifts or cañons, in all directions. Since the strata of sandstone are left nearly horizontal the effect to the eye is not as impressive as the great height would warrant. For instance, standing at the base of a cliff 4,800 feet in almost perpendicular height it was very hard to believe it was half that height—only after some time and after repeated comparisons with the shrubs and cacti could one at all realize the immensity of the rock enclosing us. . . .

The Yosemite Valley is a gem set in grandeur. It is finer than I had supposed. The photographs do not give an adequate idea of it. It is, like Norwegian scenery, on too grand a scale to be reduced to paper size. But I think the Trees have made the deepest impression upon me. California may well boast of her Trees, and they should be spelled with a capital T when they are written about.

We have set our faces eastward and are now going among the

mines. We visited the Quicksilver mine of New Almaden and we are now among the gold mines. The Hydraulic mines are stopped but we find many quartz veins still worked.

This place is an ideal mining town. They have plenty of water and each house in the village has its garden and shrubbery, while large locust and poplar trees line the streets. . . .

Robert has been for the most part quite well, but the long drives in the sun seem to tire him more than they do me. I am very strong and seem to endure all sorts of knocking about.

> 32 Eliot Street,
> JAMAICA PLAIN, MASSACHUSETTS,
> December 13, 1886.

Your letter came in the week when we dared to hope that Professor Richards was really coming back to life after three weeks of very dangerous Typhoid Pneumonia. So your imagination of the even tenor of my ways was partly correct. Robert is now down stairs and doing very nicely indeed but he had a hard time of it, the fever ran four weeks in all. I had two nurses, sent mother away and had a regular hospital with hours strictly kept so that I went out nearly every day for air and nerves. I found it made a difference and I had to keep my head level. Dr. Williams staid in the house for eight nights so I was relieved of the worst strain.

I have a very good assistant this year and so by going in for an hour or two I could keep the work going on. We also managed to plan Robert's work so the students have not suffered. Of course other outside work has been mostly put one side.

> PROVINCETOWN, July 19, 1887.

Miss Capen came down from Northampton last Thursday and I proposed to her one of our four day trips to some unexplored country of coolness and drives. We decided on the Cape as quite unknown to us although only four hours from Boston. So yesterday morning we left Jamaica Plain about half past seven and had dinner here. We walked about this queer old town and then were driven over to the life saving station, across billows of sand, through thickets of blueberry, wild pear, beech and plums, over cranberry bogs and turf roads. It is all new and interesting, this out of the way corner town, half Portuguese, half old whaling population and queer collections of houses looking as if there had been a shower of houses and they had staid where they had fallen, as some one has remarked of them. We have seen the curing of the codfish and heard how the Nova Scotia fishermen have spoiled trade.

This point is only sand, so the vessels coming home bring as ballast a load of loam for the gardens or of gravel for the streets so that Provincetown is made up of a little of everywhere.